C000010845

Scars Do Heal is one of the best novels that I have read from an African author since Chinua Achebe's *Things Fall Apart*. This spine-chilling and optimistic book is a perfect read for rejuvenation, knowledge and fun. With a fascinating plot that explores modern and global themes from love, family, marriage, perseverance to success, failure, faith and forgiveness, the novel reaches a very intense, consuming climax and a plethora of emotions when the hero takes ill shortly before a life-deciding scholarship competitive test. This leads to a fascinating denouement that will make you spellbound till the end. This is a must-have novel for all lovers of great works of fiction.

- Prof. Kọlawọle Waziri Ọlagboyega, Japan

Whether or not you have ever lived in Nigeria, *Scars Do Heal* will draw you into what it is like growing up in that great but flawed country where your life chances depend so much on the hand dealt you by your family and the education system. Issues of polygamy and discipline; sex and power; violence and forgiveness; hard work and rewards and Christian faith are all dealt with honestly and with a lightness of touch that belies their seriousness. It's a good story with plenty of depth and I like that it is not overly-sentimental. Just when you think everything is going to go right, something else goes wrong. I like all the dialogue - makes it easy to read. Above all, it encourages all of us to keep hoping for a brighter future - scars can heal.

- Neil Sorensen, Newcastle-upon-Tyne, UK

Kayọde writes a compelling tale that strongly reminds readers that scars of life can indeed heal. The pains, disappointments, and unmet expectations that life brings our way through circumstances can come together to mould us into individuals that tell the stories of battles won through courage, forgiveness, and faith. Tayọ, the protagonist in this book, will appeal to anyone who is acutely aware of how broken humanity is, yet longs for reassurance that there is hope for each one, regardless of their backstory. The story of Tayọ's struggles and victories leave a lasting impression on me. I strongly recommend this book because it's thought-provoking!

- Lanre Ilọ, Canada.

Scars Do Heal addresses factors that prevent one from achieving success in life. However, it encourages one to not despair but to hold on strongly and keep believing. The importance of not harbouring bitterness is stressed. Many times, I was drawn into some unforgettable scenes as I read the novel with rapt attention. You will find it a good read.

- Akindamọla Akinyọọla, Lagos, Nigeria.

The novel has an interesting story line. Tayọ's character and endurance are worthy of emulation. Thanks for writing about unfairness and forgiveness in the world. Everyone that will read this novel will find it very enjoyable. It's unputdownable.

- Faith Ike, Lagos, Nigeria.

Scars Do Heal, is in part, a written form of the oral storytelling which was/is still prevalent in many cultures all over the world. Reading it brings to life some aspects of Nigeria's culture which many people might have never heard of. The issues of life's journey and its unpredictability are well espoused by the author.

- Rekha Narula, Midlands, UK

SCARS DO HEAL

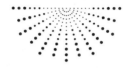

KAYODE AKINROPO

Roland Hughes

All Blessing

01-11-22

OPTIMALPATH PUBLISHING

This novel is a work of fiction. The characters, incidents, and dialogues are all products of the author's imagination. Any resemblance to real events or persons living or dead, is a coincidence

Copyright©2021 by Kayode Akinropo

All rights reserved

Published by Optimalpath Publishing. A division of Optimalpath Consulting Limited, The Beacon, Westgate Road, Newcastle upon Tyne, NE4 9PQ, United Kingdom

No part of this book may be reproduced in any form or by any electronic or mechanical means, including information storage and retrieval systems, without written permission from the author, except for the use of brief quotations in a book review

To the memory of my very dear friend, Pastor Ayọbami Oyebami.
Rest on in peace until we meet to part no more.

ACKNOWLEDGMENTS

I would like to acknowledge the following people who have helped in many special ways to make the publication of this novel a reality. I couldn't have been talking about this gift to the literary world if not for the rare encouragement given to me by Dr. Olubusọla Eshiet early this year. She insisted on my finding my manuscript where it had been dumped for many years and go to work on it. That encouragement changed the novel's life story.

I'd also like to thank the team at Optimalpath Publishing for their candid comments and suggestions all the time.

A massive thank you goes to my wonderful friends: Dr. Ayọ Banji, Faith Ike, Neil Sorensen, Prof. Kọlawọle Waziri Olagboyega, Rekha Narula, Akindamọla Akinyọọla and Lanre Ilọ who all gave their precious time to review the novel.

My appreciation goes to my amazing family - my dear wife, Iyabọde, and my children, Ọlamide and Ifẹoluwa. I call them my in-house/resident editors, proof-readers and literary critics all in one. Your frank comments and suggestions throughout the period of writing this novel are invaluable.

And finally, everlasting thanks go to my God who makes all things possible. You're worthy of all praise. Without You, no me.

CHAPTER ONE

T he end of a marriage has got to be one of the saddest events one can experience. I've heard that the pain [of divorce] is second only to an actual death in the family and that sounds about right – Danica Mckellar

"This is a plague on my household. What have I done to deserve this type of calamity? My ancestors, I hope you're not sleeping the sleep of death and forgetfulness. On your hands lies my hope," Ajanaku's father, Ifakunle, continued his lamentation after he had buried all the children borne to him by his six wives.

"If you want a child to live after you, you have to sacrifice your own life," the *Ifá* priest began.

"What did you say? Did I hear you well? How will that bring all the children that died back to life?"

"Be patient Ifakunle. You heard what I said correctly. That's what the gods have asked me to tell you. That you have to sacrifice your own life to have a child who will succeed you."

"Are you saying a dead man can bear a child or what do you….?" Ifakunle asked.

"My child, this is what the gods have said you should do. Go and get one of your wives impregnated as soon as you can. I say one. When the foetus is six months' old, terminate your life and the child will live. Does this make any sense to you now?"

"Uh-huh! Uh-huh! Uh-huh! What a dilemma! In my society, coming to this life without leaving a child as your successor is an exercise in futility. Just a waste. Why should this happen to me?" he murmured to himself.

"What is your choice?" the *Ifá* priest asked.

"On this one, I think their wish is my command but, em...em...em.... This world is terrible. Rich or poor, you lose when you look at everything carefully and think deep. Hum…."

"I think you're very correct if your submission is carefully considered. As rich and famous as you are, you shouldn't die without a living child to bear your name forever."

"You're right Baba. That's what I was thinking."

And so, Ajanaku was born. As the gods said, he grew up and inherited everything that belonged to his father. With all the wealth bestowed on him, advising or trying to stop him from marrying many wives and having many children was very difficult. Fortunately for him, all his children survived. For him, life had been fair enough. His second wife gave birth to six children and the only male among them was Kọlapọ.

When Ajanaku was getting old, he called some trusted elders in his village one day and told them, "Please, death doesn't give any notice. You're my eyes. You're my ears. You're my kinsmen. Whenever I die and I'm no more, do justice to all I have. Give my children enough of my inheritance to banish poverty from their lives. The rest should go to my wives and other family members. Please do this and I will rest in peace."

"What's this you're saying Ajanaku? Twenty, thirty, fifty years to come, you'll still be here with us. Why are you wishing yourself death at this time of your life?" one of the elders asked.

"Hum….I know what I'm talking about. You can tell so many other things with some degree of certainty but you can't tell the time you'll die, can you? No. None of us can. Right? Whenever death comes, so be it. The gods have blessed me, and I thank them for that. Be witnesses to all I have said today." Many years later, Ajanaku died. Kọlapọ, being his mother's only son received tangible inheritance from his father's wealth. He also married many wives as there was enough money to take care of all of them and their children. Ọmọtayọ, ('Tayọ' for short) was born after his mother had given birth to three girls which was not something valued in their custom where male children were much more preferred. Tayọ's birth brought some joy to his parents but just for a short time.

Whereas some children were born lucky into peaceful, loving, and rich homes, his was the opposite. The three did not co-exist. Barely a year after his birth, serious misunderstanding crept into his parents' home. For young Tayọ and his sisters, grimness mingled with grief and sorrow as they witnessed what happened in a home where there was no peace of mind.

Tayọ's father, Kọlapọ, kept acquiring women for the fun of it. Like other wealthy men in his area, he saw it as an honour and a competition. For the men, the more the merrier. When he married his fourth wife, real trouble started in his home and the centre could no longer hold. After much problem, Tayọ's mother, Ọmọyẹ, the first wife, left her matrimonial home unceremoniously with her children. She went straight back to her parents' village. She told her parents who were already aware of the problems in her marriage that she had had enough. She insisted there was no way she would go back to her husband unless they wanted her dead.

They listened sympathetically to her and promised to invite her husband for a discussion on a possible solution considering the fate of her children. She would probably leave them with her husband and their stepmothers. The meeting between Tayọ's father and his in-laws was held. Kọlapọ, accompanied by some of his relations came to the meeting. After they had exchanged greetings, they settled down for the business of the day.

Ọmọyẹ's father asked his daughter, "Your husband and his people are here, can you tell this sitting the reasons you left your husband and came back to us?"

She knelt down and thanked everyone for giving their time to be present and said, "Since my husband married additional wives, things have not been the same. He hardly talks to me and my children, neither does he provide for us. We used to be one family, but the younger wives are the ones calling the tune now. Whatever they say is final in our home. His other wives lie against one another and me every time. My husband supports them even when what they say about me is not true. One even accused me of being responsible for her barrenness. I told my husband about the allegation and to date, he has not done anything about it. Instead, his wife warned me to stop reporting her to our husband. Any little misunderstanding between us snowballs into serious issues these days. All these give me sleepless nights. Before I suddenly die of depression and all of you will ask the cause of my death, I want you to help and appeal to my husband to have a talk with his wives for them to have a change of heart. It's possible for all of us to live together. We have all done that for a short time. If he takes control of his home, I think things can get back to normal."

"Have you finished Ọmọyẹ?" her father asked.

"Yes Baba."

"We have all heard what Ọmọyẹ said. I want her husband to respond to all she has alleged. Over to you Kọlapọ."

"Thank you all for coming today," Kọlapọ began. "Ọmọyẹ, my wife, lies a lot. Yes, I might not be providing all my wives and their children enough to sustain them at present but I'm trying my best in the current circumstances I find myself. My business is not doing well; my debtors are not paying back, and my creditors are on my neck. As we all know, the weather has not been fair to farmers in the last few years. I was thinking things will get better but here we are. She warned me not to marry more wives. I told her that was exactly what I was going to do. I did it. But since I married my second wife and other wives, there has not been peace in my house. She's jealous and dangerous. It is either this problem or the other from this troublesome and most senior wife of mine. As the first wife, I appealed to her to act with wisdom, but she never wanted to hear that. She is trying to poison her children's minds against me. That hurts me a lot. Now…."

"You are a terrible liar. All you're doing now is to shift all the blame on me. This I will not accept," Ọmọyẹ furiously cut in.

"You can all now see her stupid behaviour. No respect for anybody," Kọlapọ said.

"You call me stupid even here in my father's house. You are stupid too," Ọmọyẹ said as she left the gathering in annoyance. Her father ordered her to come back but she refused.

"Kọlapọ, you're rude to us your in-laws. You came here and, in our presence, you called our daughter 'stupid'. We can't accept that kind of behaviour from you. In essence, you're saying we are 'stupid'. Isn't that correct? Could you apologise now before we go further," Ọmọyẹ's father ordered.

As Kọlapọ's relatives were signalling to him to do as he was asked to, he stood up and left the meeting. Because of the way both Kọlapọ and Ọmọyẹ behaved, the meeting yielded no useful solution that day. In fact, Kọlapọ did not leave the village with his relations who accompanied him to the meeting. He abandoned them when the issue at stake became irreconcilable. His family tried to beg his in-laws on his behalf but there was no resolution.

After Kọlapọ and all his people had left, Ọmọyẹ's parents scolded her for behaving the way she did during the meeting. They told her that she should have allowed them to speak instead of exchanging words with her husband. She was angry that they did not support her as she had wanted. One day without a word about her destination, she left her parents' village. She abandoned Tayọ and his three sisters, Dayọ, Dupẹ and Ikẹoluwa ('Ikẹ' for short) with her parents. Her family tried hard to find out her whereabouts, but they did not succeed.

"Ọmọyẹ, you have not done well at all. There are bound to be problems in any family relationship which could be solved amicably but running away has never been a solution. You ran away from your family. You ran away from your own children. I pray that wherever you are, my ancestors will keep you safe and bring you back to us very soon," her mother talked to herself as she sat down alone one day.

So early, Tayọ and his sisters started life in most uncertain circumstances. They were directionless as they were denied direct parental care. Tayọ's maternal grandmother had no choice but to take care of Tayọ and his sisters. It was tough; she and her grandchildren endured untold hardship because of poverty. Having three square meals was a luxury as she depended on her feeding allocation from her husband to take care of herself and her grandchildren.

As the children continued to grow, villagers started gossiping about them and their future.

"Won't Ọmọyẹ's children go to school or learn a trade," a woman asked her husband when she saw all of them going to the farm one day.

"But that's their family's problem. It isn't ours, is it? her husband responded.

"Well, I'm just thinking about it."

"Please, think about other better things instead."

Another villager also once asked Tayọ's grandmother why the girls had not started school. Her response was short and sharp.

"Girls are supposed to be of little knowledge to be useful to their husbands. Only boys must seek high knowledge. Even for that, too much learning is madness for any person."

Since that day, nobody inquired about why the girls were not sent to school especially when their father who could let it happen just kept mute. Ikẹ, one of Tayọ's three sisters was taken away by her mother's first cousin, Ezekiel, to live with him. But none of her siblings heard any information about her for a long time.

Tayọ clocked six and he was supposed to start primary school at that age. The teachers visited his village, Kufi, during the holidays to register children of school age for the following school year. The message of whether Tayọ would start school was communicated to his father. When he got it, he declined to make any comment. The inability of his in-laws to bring back his wife was, according to him, a testimony of their conspiracy in his wife's defection from their village.

When he later decided to make his views known to his in-laws, it was sharp and confrontational. "The girls may be living here with you, but Tayọ cannot start school in your village." His standoff angered his in-laws. This started another quarrel between both parties. The more the people from both sides tried to settle that life-deciding issue for Tayọ, the harder it became.

Tayọ was too young to understand what the problem was all about, but he was not happy seeing his age mates on their way to school every day. Unknown to him, he was being denied going to school at the right age by two opposing camps - his father and his father's in-laws. His father asked him to be released to him so he could send him to school in his village; his in-laws vowed not to release him unless his father paid all that they had spent on him since his mother left.

"Tayọ won't be sent to school in any of the two villages," his grandmother once said emphatically. "If he does not go to school, this problem of when and where to start school will be solved once and for all."

His father was called an ingrate for his failure to show any appreciation for all that had been done for his children after his separation from his wife. Like sworn enemies, Kọlapọ was embroiled in an unending quarrel with his in-laws for many years. All those years, Tayọ watched the scene with childish innocence as his sisters' and his future was being wasted.

The only person who might be able to resolve the heated argument was his mother, but no one knew her whereabouts. She never came to check how her children were doing. To make matters worse, Tayọ's education and possibly that of his sisters that could have been guaranteed if she was with them was not given any tangible consideration by their father and their grandparents.

Elders from both feuding families met again at Tayọ's grandparents' village as usual when Tayọ was eight years old. They tried to find a truce. Again, the meeting was disastrous. Tayọ was brought into the centre of their gathering. Prayers, according to their tradition, were offered before the meeting commenced so God could direct them. Though he listened with rapt attention to the contention of both parties, he did not understand all their arguments and counter arguments. What he wanted was to be allowed to start school, but instead, there was disharmony each time the issue was debated.

"Who is the true owner of a child according to our custom?" asked one of Kọlapọ's relatives. As expected, this question sparked off a big row.

"If that's what you want to claim, a mother owns a child," a woman from Tayọ's mother's village responded angrily.

"Ok. Let's agree that's true, where is the mother now?" a man countered the woman's response despite attempts to hush him. These exchanges of counter views soon degenerated into a serious altercation. At that juncture and like at the Tower of Babel, discordant chanting set in. What could have turned out to be a very messy situation was averted when Kọlapọ and his people stormed out of the meeting. Tayọ and his sisters started crying. They were not asked to make any comment and they did not utter a word.

"Will I ever go to school like my age mates? Why has my going to school become this difficult?" he asked his elder sisters.

When Tayọ was nine, the war of nerves had cooled down on both sides. Village heads arranged another meeting. It was to take place in a neutral village. Initially his father's in-laws refused to welcome such a meeting but after much persuasion from the meeting conferees, they agreed to take part. It was a large gathering. Tayọ, the unfortunate boy, was again brought into the centre of the gathering as it was done during the other meetings. His father's family sat opposite their in-laws. The elders sat in the middle to prevent unnecessary confrontation from both sides.

The most senior of the village heads prayed. After the prayers, he talked at great length and appealed to both parties. He said, "It is necessary we all do everything with patience, wisdom and understanding today. We should have at the back of our mind the implication of what we're doing on this innocent boy. If we cannot help him today, will he ever forgive us when he grows up and learns about what prevented him from going to school like his friends? Indirectly, we're doing ourselves a disservice if we fail to iron out this problem. And the earlier we do this the better. Let's forgive and forget all that has happened." Before he finished his speech, many of them knew that the case might be heading for a positive end. It was as if their ancestors directly intervened that day. Without any invitation of comments from either side, the man pronounced, "Tayọ must start school at his mother's village this year. You, Kọlapọ, his father, must buy books, uniform and other school materials for him as long as he attends school every school year. Not only this, but you must also pay any fees that the school may levy at any time during his studies. Feel free to bring food items to your in-laws to take care of your children. After all said and done, they are still your children. When Tayọ finishes his primary education, we shall sit again and decide the way forward for him. His sisters can learn trade if they want to or get married anytime they are ready for that. I thank all of you for honouring our invitation. I thank you, Kọlapọ, your family members and especially, you, Kọlapọ's in-laws. Our ancestors will continue to honour all of you."

As the man finished his last statement, Kọlapọ was about to say something but the applause which greeted the old man's message instantly suppressed his intention. It appeared everybody was satisfied. He prostrated himself before his in-laws, thanked the elders and left with his relatives. For the first time, an agreement was reached. Tayọ was very happy as he was assured of starting school at the start of the following school session. His two sisters who were also there felt happy that their brother would start school but at the same time, they were not pleased that the elderly peace maker relegated them to the back seat.

"I'll start school this year," Tayọ told his friends when he got back to the village. "I'll be in the same class with all of you because we're age mates." His friend laughed at his ignorance.

"Why are you laughing Kunle? What's funny about that?" he asked.

"Nothing," his friend replied and laughed again. Kunle knew he and Tayo's other friends were already ahead of him as far as class level was concerned. His behaviour upset Tayọ.

At the beginning of the new school session, he started school. He was very happy that God had eventually changed the unyielding attitude of his father and his grandparents.

There were many villages that made up Tayọ's locality which was one of the areas in Ibadan Metropolitan City. Ibadan was the capital city of the old western region of Nigeria. It was the third-largest city by population and the largest city by geographical area in Nigeria after Lagos and Kano. It was created around 1829 as a war camp for warriors. During the time of the missionaries' work in Ibadan and its environs, they always established a school and a church in the same village they chose for that purpose. They were interested in introducing Christianity and western education to the people. They believed the way to achieve their aim was to Christianise and educate as many local people as possible who would help them to win souls for Christ. They thought indigenes would trust their own people more than the foreigners in their midst. The only primary school, Saint Peter's Anglican Primary School, Lakinde, was established beside a church. It was quite a big school but a far distance from Tayọ's village. Pupils from many villages often trekked long distances to and from school. That was why age was a pre-requisite for starting schooling. People also went very far distances to fetch water for domestic use from rivers especially during the dry season. Rainy season was a comfort to them. Unlike in the city, there were no vehicles for commercial purposes. Moreover, most of the villagers detested travelling by vehicles as they were seen as agents of death especially when accidents happened. To them, trekking long distances was one of the enjoyments in the lives of the local people. In fact, they believed walking long distances gave them longevity.

Kọlapọ complied with the directives the old man gave. A week before the school resumption day, Tayọ was full of great expectation.

"I hope that the food vendor you often talked about would sell rice and beans to me during break time," Tayọ inquired from Kunle when they were playing one day.

"She would, provided you have your money," Kunle responded.

"Do they beat you at school?" Tayọ asked.

"Yes, they do but for some reasons. For example, if you make a noise, fight, steal or come late to school, the teachers will beat you."

"Kunle, is the cane the teachers use as long and strong like that normally used by my grandfather?" he asked.

He wanted to know whether he was going to another dreadful place like home where corporal punishment was the order of the day for any committed offences.

"No," Kunle allayed his fear.

Tayọ's grandfather was tall and heavily built. He was a rich farmer who married many wives. He was a disciplinarian. Often, he would cut fresh canes during the dry season; get them dried and keep them to be used for the whole year to beat any of his disobedient children. The canes were always kept near him in case any emergency whipping was required. The man smoked tobacco. Some of Tayọ's main duties every day were to supply soot from the fire to light the pipe for the tobacco, go to other villages at times to buy palm wine and accompany the old man to the farm. They were his allocated jobs. Going to the farm was one of the

things Tayọ hated most especially during the rainy season
when everywhere would be wet and muddy. That was one
of the reasons he was looking forward to going to school;
he wanted to avoid being a farmer in future. Tayọ's major
hobby, football, always came into conflict with his duties to
his grandfather. He might be playing football with his
friends but once he was called upon, he must be ready to
leave the playing ground to supply soot for his grandfather's
pipe. Others would either wait for him or continue playing.
God help him if he was called and he was nowhere to be
found. He would be beaten mercilessly by his grandfather.
He was not alone in that misfortune of receiving serious
beating. If any of the man's biological children committed
any offence even if they were married, the old man would
not hesitate to mete out the usual beating to them.

One day, an event occurred which led to Tayọ getting
punished severely. It was getting to the night when his
grandfather asked him to go and fetch some firewood from
the farm. He could not go alone because it was already
getting dark, but he did not have the confidence to tell the
old man. He left for one of his friends' houses. He begged
Biyi, his friend, to accompany him to fetch the firewood,
but he declined. That time, nobody was present in the
house. There was one big parlour decorated with many
black and white photo frames of Biyi's family. They were
cherished by his father because they had been there for
many generations with history behind each of them. As fate
would have it, another friend of Tayọ brought a ball and in a

jiffy, the parlour was turned into another Wembley Stadium. The ball was played to Tayọ. He forgot that they were in an enclosed place. He kicked the ball hard and it hit some of the frames. They fell and broke into pieces. Immediately all the players ran out of the building.

The man came back and met the broken photo frames all over the place. He was terribly annoyed. He thought his son was the culprit as he had warned him before not to play football in any area of their house.

He yelled, "Biyi, go and bring my cane, come and lie down here to receive your punishment for being a very destructive element. You've used your ball again to cause a havoc. I've told you to stop wasting your time playing football, but you will never stop."

Before his father could finish, Biyi was crying. He said, "Sorry *Baba*, sorry, sorry, it was Tayọ who broke the photo frames, not me. I was outside the house when it all happened. I don't play football in the house anymore."

When his father heard that, he went straight to Tayọ's grandfather's house and reported him.

"Good day Baba. I have come to report Tayọ to you. I got back home now and I found out some photo frames in my house have been smashed by these stubborn boys who do not know anything more than playing football at anytime and anywhere. The one that annoyed me most is the photo frame which my father handed over to me to keep. If this incident repeats itself, I will ask Tayọ never to step into my house again. But I have come so you will not take offence when I do that."

Tayọ's grandfather apologised to the man and told him it was firewood he asked Tayọ to go and fetch but that he had not seen him since then.

"You will hear from me after I have punished him for being such a stubborn boy. Once again, accept my apology."

"That's okay Baba. Good day."

"Mama Ọmọyẹ. Mama Ọmọyẹ. Mama Ọmọyẹ...," Tayọ's grandfather called his wife.

"Is everything okay?" his wife asked.

"No. Your grandson, Tayọ, went to Ajagbe's house and destroyed all the photo frames in his parlour when he was playing football there with some of his friends. Ajagbe came here few minutes ago to report what happened in his house to me. Didn't you see him?"

"No. But I thought you said you sent Tayọ to the farm to go and fetch some firewood."

"Exactly. That's why I will make sure he suffers for being disobedient. Can you call him for me?"

"I don't even know where he has gone to in the last few hours. I will try to look for him as he must be hiding somewhere now," grandmother said as she was leaving her husband's room.

She knew serious punishment awaited Tayọ. Her husband did not joke with issues like that. His grandmother and others looked all around for him but could not find him. They later concluded that he might have gone to another village to sleep with any of his friends because of fear of the punishment waiting for him at home. All that time they were looking for him, he had gone to hide inside their kitchen in the dark on a wooden plank. He slept off as he had become too tired and confused by the unwelcome situation in which he had put himself. He woke up a minute after midnight. He felt dead with fright. He was afraid of the darkness as he had heard so many stories about ghosts and other sinister spirits that walked about during the night. He ran out from his hiding, fell, stood up and went straight to the door that led to their house. He banged the door and cried out in fear. His grandmother and other house members knew he was the one. She came out and opened the door for him to come in. She was short for words. Without any question on what had happened the previous day, she asked him to come in and sleep in her room. She behaved as if she was not aware of the atrocity he had committed. Tayọ often slept in the same room with his grandfather, but that early morning, he did not approach his grandfather's room. He knew he would face two serious charges: failure to fetch firewood and breaking of photo frames in another man's house.

Around six o'clock in the morning, his grandfather came very silently to his wife's room where Tayọ was sleeping. He woke Tayọ up, took him by the hand and led him to his room. Like a caught armed robber in their locality, Tayọ knew the game was up for him. He cried and begged his grandmother to save him from imminent Armageddon, but she was helpless. She knew if she made any attempt and begged on Tayọ's behalf, she too could be beaten. All the same, she begged her husband,

"Please Baba Ọmọyẹ. I know Tayọ has done something wrong, but it is too early in the morning to beat him. Please do this later."

Her husband did not say a word in response to her appeal.

"Baba, please I'm sorry. I won't do it again. Please. Please. Please, it's too early. Please Baba…. beat me later," Tayọ continued to beg his grandfather as he was being dragged along to his room. By the time they got to the man's room, Tayọ was naked as his cover cloth had fallen off him. Everybody was woken up by his noise but none could directly come to his rescue. His grandfather locked the door and brought out his dried canes.

"Where did I send you yesterday?" he asked in his croaky voice.

"Fi……….re…………….fi…………re……………woods.
Oh……Oh…………. Please o Baba. It's fi……re woooood o.

God come down and help me this morning. I am dead today oooooooooooo."

"Keep quiet. Just answer my questions. Where is the firewood?"

"Not here, Baba. It is in the…."

"Now, what happened at Ajagbe's house?"

"Baba, sorry, I will tell you. Sorry Baba, I will tell."

"You won't tell the truth, I know you. Why did you go and break his family's photo frames in his house? Did he invite you to come and play football in his house? When did his house become a playing field?" At the end of these questions, Tayọ had received no fewer than twelve strokes of the cane.

"Now," his grandfather ordered, "Lie down flat for your proper punishment for being a disobedient boy. Next time, you will never disobey me." Tayọ had no choice but to do as he was commanded. He lay down trembling and shouting with the last energy left in him.

"Baba, you want to kill this boy this morning?" People outside his locked room were asking and shouting. He never bothered. Tayọ had fainted before the man completed his satanic beating. Some family members who gathered at the entrance to his room begging him to temper justice with mercy felt pity for Tayọ though they knew what he did was wrong. When Tayọ suddenly became embarrassingly quiet, his grandfather opened the door and asked his wife to come in and take him out.

"Baba, you are wicked. This is not good," his wife said. All of them were terrified when they saw blood gushing out of Tayọ's almost lifeless body. People who were already helpless kept on shouting his name, "Tayọ! Tayọ! Tayọ! Tayọ! Please, Tayọ, answer us. We love you, please, answer us. Everybody please help. Do something now. This boy must not die here."

"Please go and call somebody to come and quickly take Tayọ to a clinic before he dies," someone suggested.

Some people rushed out to see if they could get someone to do that. As they were running helter-skelter for help, Tayọ lay on the floor as water was poured on him to help him come round. The water poured, mixed with his blood, gave a gory sight. A native doctor in their village who was informed of what had happened, came to where Tayọ was and started chanting some incantation. After doing that for about ten minutes, he called out loud, "Tayọ. Tayọ. Tayọ, receive your life back. You are not dying."

Maybe it was a coincidence, Tayọ opened his eyes gently and moved his hands. He started crying. Everyone was happy for him and thanked the native doctor for bringing Tayọ back to life. The native doctor told his grandmother as Tayọ regained some consciousness to bring some palm oil to cool his wounds. He rubbed the palm oil onto his wounds and asked her to go and buy a special herb in the market that day which would bring quick healing to his injuries. Later, his grandmother and other women gently washed his body to clear it of blood and palm oil. The native doctor said he would need to see Tayọ's grandfather to know why he had treated such a young boy in such an appalling way. To him, what Baba did to Tayọ was just pure barbaric jungle justice. Everyone urged him to do exactly that.

When Tayọ was able to talk properly, he asked

"But why did Grandfather want to kill me? Why? I am in pain."

"Sorry my son. He didn't want to kill you but when he is angry, all of us know he is always a dangerous old man. Tayọ, sorry," his grandmother said. "The native doctor has gone in to see him and talk sense into him which none of us can do."

Tayọ told Kunle that each time he remembered that beating, he wished he had died that day or in the alternative that God should have given him some power so he too could have inflicted some horrible injuries on his grandfather in retaliation for what he did to him.

Since then, Tayọ feared canes like a fully loaded gun pointed to his head. He always shied away from anything that would make his grandfather punish him. When Kunle told him that their teachers would never cane pupils like his grandfather did, he was happy to hear that.

CHAPTER TWO

T o want to learn, to have the capacity to learn, and not to be able to is a tragedy - Unknown

The school resumption day came. Tayọ could not sleep throughout the preceding night. He was thinking, "*So, I will start school at last? I will not go to school late. If others are not ready, I will leave them and go. I won't want the teachers to cane me. If teachers give me homework, I will make sure I take my time and do it well but if I don't understand what I'm asked to do, I'll take it to anyone of my friends who may know it better than I do in our village to help me out. Hum, I love school. How will my class look like? Will our teachers be friendly as I have often been told? I will love to play football for my school and help them beat other schools whenever we compete with them. Will I be scared of anything at school?*"

When morning dawned, he woke up very early. He bathed, put his uniform on but no school shoes because none was

bought for him. He went to each of the pupil's house to call
them out as he had seen some of them doing before. He
went to school barefooted but he was less bothered because
the joy of starting school had overridden other thoughts.
Six other children started school from his village that day,
but he was older than all of them.

They got to the school at the right time. The teachers were
especially happy to see the newcomers. They were asked to
be on a line and their names were written in the register.
They were encouraged to be regular and punctual. They
were instructed on punishable offences. The assembly
ended and joyfully, they all sang on their way to their
different classes. Tayọ was pleased to see the school band-
set. He loved colourful photographs of musical instruments,
animals, musicians, footballers, doctors, police officers and
many other different people and things that were hung on
the school walls. In fact, the neat classrooms, plastered walls
and other added murals inside and outside the classes drew
pupils to the school.

The class teacher entered Tayọ's classroom and met them
making a noise. When they saw him, they kept quiet. The
teacher said, "Good morning pupils. I would like to tell you
some class rules you need to obey. If any visitor enters your
class, what do you say?"

Nobody answered. When none of them responded, the
teacher said, "All of you will stand up and say, 'Good

morning sir," if he is a man like me and "Good morning ma," if she is a woman. Is that right?"

"Yes sir," they all shouted.

"Now," the teacher continued, "stand up and greet."

"Good morning sir, ma." He identified those who made mistakes by saying 'sir, ma'. He explained to them again the right way to greet. That was the first thing the teacher taught them that morning. "Now, is there anyone of you who can try and read A B C to Z?" Tayọ raised his hand. He was the only one who signified to try. The teacher told him that he would say, "I sir" next time. He had learnt some letters of the English alphabet and how to count number from his friends whenever they were reading at home. With ease, he read alphabet 'A' to 'J'. The teacher was happy and he directed others to clap for him.

"Well done. What is your name?" the teacher asked.

"Ọmọtayọ Sam Kọlapọ."

Two weeks after, their class teacher appointed Tayọ as the class monitor. His duties as specified by the teacher included asking other pupils to greet any teacher that came to their class, cleaning the chalkboard, leading his mates out during break time and making sure the chair and table for the teacher were clean. He encouraged him to work hard in his studies and come out on top of the class in class exercises, tests and exams. Tayọ followed the rules like the

Ten Commandments given to Moses. He enjoyed the work
at school unlike the work at home and in the farm.

In term and sessional examinations, in primary one, he took
the first position twice and second position once. Ṭayọ was
not happy when he came second. He was told that the girl
who took the first position got just two marks more than he
did. He believed that the girl was brilliant but not as
brilliant as he was. He thought the teacher would appoint
the girl as the monitor but the teacher did not.

He was promoted to primary two and came first in all the
examinations. He maintained his academic record and
remained the class monitor. He often read alone at home
whenever he got the opportunity. He did this because at the
end of each session, prizes were given out to those who
took the first three positions in each class. For him, that
prize was a must to get each year. So, he worked very hard
for it. In primary three, much was demanded from them.
For example, they were given portions to cut during
gardening, they were to come to school every Monday with
a bundle of broom and a bundle of firewood for the
teachers. Unlike in primary one and two, they were
punished when they came late to school and if anyone of
them went against the school rules and regulations, they
were caned as well. With all these, Ṭayọ found out that
school, after all, was not a bed of roses.

By that time, his father, though happy with his son's school
academic performances, was getting tired of financing his

education. At times, his uniform would tear off before another one would be bought for him. His father would have to be begged before his books were bought. So soon, the directives of the old man who settled the rift before he started school were disobeyed at will. If pupils were asked to pay any school or church levy, he would be one of those who would pay last. Each day during the school assembly, the names of debtors were usually called out by the headmaster who at times would give them some strokes of the cane so that they would remind their parents when they got home to make payment. Tayọ did not like being asked to come out as one of the pupils owing the school. His father did not like the situation either, but he was not as rich as he used to be as he had told his in-laws during one of the meetings. One day he came personally to the school and begged the headteacher to give him more time to settle Tayọ's school fees. The headteacher agreed and never asked him to come out as a debtor till his father fulfilled his promise.

During church festivals especially Christmas, Easter and Children's Harvest Day, new clothes were always bought for the children by their parents. For Tayọ, his own would be either purchased on credit by his grandmother or be left out completely. He and his sisters would go to the church in old clothes and with no shoes to wear. If Tayọ's mother had shown up, things could have maybe turned out better. But even at his age then, Tayọ would not recognise his mother if he met her by chance somewhere. He always cried when he saw his mates in new dresses. In the village, he could not find peace. Abusive words were always heaped on him by many people at the slightest provocation simply because of his absentee mother. He was the object of ridicule.

He was fighting with one boy in his village one day when the boy insulted him. The boy told him his mother ran away because he was a bad boy who had brought bad luck to his family when he was born. This angered Tayọ. He beat the boy up. The boy's mother came and asked Tayọ what her son had done to him. When Tayọ explained what happened between the two of them to the woman, she said

"Is my son lying? Do you know where your mother is? You're a bad boy as my son has said. Next time this happens, you'll be in trouble."

Tayọ went straight to his grandmother dejected. He reported what the woman said to her. She pacified him and said,

"Don't mind her, very soon your mother would come back home to see all of us and all of them will be put to shame. I'll go later and warn her never to say something like that to you again."

That gave Tayọ some hope but still, he fought with those he could challenge whenever he was abused because of what his mother did.

Tayọ's sister, Modupẹ ('Dupẹ for short) started primary school without the approval of any of her parents and grandparents. Unlike the reasoning of Tayọ's father and grandparents concerning female children and schooling, some parents in their area sent their male and female children to school. Dupẹ was sixteen years old when she started primary school.

She could not have dreamed of going to school if not for an event that happened one day between her and Ikẹ, her younger sister. Their eldest sister, Dayọ had been married off once she was in her early twenties. During a third term holiday, Ikẹ arrived in the village without prior notice. Tayọ was the first person to notice the visitor but could not recognise her well because she dressed gaily and her stature had changed greatly. She was coming directly to their house which she had not stepped in since she left the village with their uncle who promised to take care of her. When she was a few metres away, Tayọ recognised that she was Ikẹ. He shouted her name, ran and embraced her. She too was happy to see him.

Tayọ said, "I am very happy to see you Ikẹ. You are looking fine. You must be enjoying there, unlike here. Look how beautiful you are in your dress. Do you go to school?"

"Thank you Tayọ. Wait, I'll answer all your questions. First, where are our grandparents, sisters Dayọ and Dupẹ?" she asked.

"Grandparents have gone to the farm with Dupẹ. Sister Dayọ is now married. I'm at home because Grandfather sent me on an errand this morning. If not, you wouldn't have met any of us at home."

"So, sister Dayọ is married?"

"Long time ago. Were you not told? She didn't want to get married but she was forced to. She cried and cried for days but no one listened to her. Don't tell anybody I told you this."

"No. We were not informed at all."

"How is our father doing?"

"At times, he comes here to see us and bring some foodstuff along."

"In which class are you?"

"Primary 4. I will be going to primary 5 next session."

"Are you enjoying school?" Ikẹ asked.

"Yes, I am."

"Sister Dupẹ should be in secondary school, correct?"

"Ah…. ah….ah, secondary what? She is not allowed to go to school. Sister Dayọ did not attend any school before she got married," he explained.

"Did they say they didn't like to go to school or what happened?" Ikẹ inquired.

"No. My father and our grandparents said girls should not go after book knowledge like boys."

"Are you saying no single girl goes to school in this village?" Ikẹ asked.

"That is not it. Parents are different, you know. Even in this village, few girls are allowed to go to school."

"But this is too bad," Ikẹ said.

"In which class are you now, Ikẹ?" Tayọ asked her because from her appearance and the way she spoke, he knew she must be attending school.

"I'm going to Form 3 in my secondary school next session."

"Who provides for your school expenses?"

"Uncle Ezekiel, of course."

"He must be a very nice man."

"He is not only nice but knows the value of education. All his children go to school," Ikẹ said of her uncle with pride. After some few minutes, she left Tayọ and other children to go and greet the entire villagers as their customs demanded. They were very happy to see her. When she got back, she opened her bag and brought out packets of sweet. She gave sweets to all the children who had congregated to welcome their new visitor, and get whatever she might have brought as gifts. Many of them left immediately they got their own sweet. Those villagers who were not around when Ikẹ arrived got the news of her arrival from their wards. For the rest of the day, it was one well-wisher or the other coming to see and greet her.

All this while, Tayọ was thinking about different types of parents. Some, to him were good while some were not at all caring. He thought that if Ikẹ had stayed with them in that village, she might never have gone to school either because of the disagreement between their father and his in-laws or the general belief among the people that a woman's education was in the kitchen.

"When was the last time our mother came on a visit to see you?"

"She has never come to this place since she left us. The worst part of it is that till date nobody knows where she lives."

"Is she dead or what?" Ikẹ asked.

"No. One *Ifá* priest once told our grandmother that her daughter is still alive and that she will come back home one day. That day, neither the soothsayer nor anyone could tell."

"Ikẹ, do you know that some women who separated from their husbands like our mother still come here to see their children? Not that alone, they buy many beautiful things for them all the time to make them happy."

That statement made Ikẹ to be very sad. Tayọ was saying everything emotionally. Instead of responding, Ikẹ was moved to tears. Tayọ kept quiet when he noted he was making his sister uncomfortable.

Grandfather came back from the farm first. Tayọ went to tell him straight away that Ikẹ had come to see them. As he was doing that, Ikẹ entered Grandfather's spacious living room, knelt very close to where he was sitting and greeted him. He welcomed her warmly and asked after her uncle. He asked if she had eaten anything since she arrived.

Ikẹ said, "No Baba, food could wait until Mama and Dupẹ come back. I'm eager to see them since all these days."

"That's ok my daughter."

Ikẹ had been in the village for some hours when Grandmother and Dupẹ arrived from the farm. Once Tayọ heard their voices, he quickly left Ikẹ and ran to meet them on the way before Ikẹ knew what was happening.

"Do you know what, Ikẹ is around," Tayọ announced gladly.

"Which Ikẹ?" Dupẹ and Grandmother asked.

"My sister living with Uncle Ezekiel," he told them.

They were both surprised and wondered if Tayọ knew what he was talking about. But in front of them was Ikẹ coming to meet them. Dupẹ put down her load, ran and embraced her. Ikẹ knelt to greet Grandmother right there on the road. Grandmother drew her close and showered oriki[1] on her. Tayọ observed that Dupẹ was looking at Ikẹ's beautiful dress and smooth skin with keen interest.

Tayọ tapped Dupẹ and said, "Can't you see, Ikẹ is enjoying where she is living." Dupẹ did not say anything. They went into the house and put the farm products down. Grandmother asked Ikẹ to change her dress. She told them she was around to spend few days with them because she was on holiday.

"So, you go to school?" grandmother asked.

"Yes Mama," Ikẹ replied.

"I thank God and I thank Ezekiel. It shall be well with all of you. You'll be so rich and take me to America to see the Queen."

"Amen. But Mama, the Queen does not live in America but in London."

"My daughter, that is still ok. Take me to wherever the Queen lives. I will like to meet her." Dupẹ and Tayọ wondered why Grandmother who always said girls should not be educated saw nothing wrong in Ikẹ's case and why she admired the Queen who was the head of state of a country.

Early in the morning of the fourth day of Ikẹ's arrival, Grandmother went to visit her family in another village. She instructed Tayọ and his sisters what to do and told them the time she would come back that day. They were happy knowing full well they would have the chance to talk on many issues which if she were around, they could never do. When they were together in the room, Ikẹ looked all around and said

"Sister Dupẹ, I was told by Tayọ when I arrived here that you don't go to school. He told me that our father and our grandparents are not interested in girls' education. Is that right?"

"Yes, that's right. I thought I would go to school but that never came to be," Dupe explained, her voice trembling.

"But don't we have another uncle that you can run to who will send you to school like Uncle Ezekiel has done for Ikẹ?" Tayọ asked though the answer was meant for Ikẹ.

"Sister, you are almost sixteen years old now. Can you start school if you find someone to send you?" Ikẹ asked.

Dupẹ thought for some minutes and said,

"I will go. I will be happy to go to school. But these people will never allow me to go to school. I know them well. I have painfully accepted this as my fate but if the chance comes, I will."

"When I get back home, I will explain your plight to my uncle and see if there's any way he could help. He is someone who believes so much in education for every child. I know he will try," Ikẹ assured Dupẹ with all seriousness. Like a rainbow in the sky, Dupẹ became animated with sudden joy as she thought what that would mean for her.

"Tayọ, please make sure you don't tell Grandmother or anybody about what we have just discussed, and I will give you something in return for that. Do you promise you won't?"

"Yes, I promise. I won't tell anyone but what will you give me in return for keeping this as a secret?"

"Don't worry, I'll keep my promise, okay?" Ikẹ said, fearing Tayọ might let the cat out of the bag. Whenever Ikẹ and Tayọ discussed any school events, Dupẹ always looked at them with keen interest. She longed earnestly to experience school life one day.

"Do you know something Ikẹ? Tayọ asked.

"No, I don't. What is it?"

"Do you know I am the class monitor for my class."

"That's good to hear. Well done, Tayọ. Tell me, how did it happen?"

"On the first day in our class, our class teacher asked if any of us could read the English alphabet A to Z. I raised my hand and he asked me to try. I think I was only able to read 'A' to 'J'. The teacher was very happy with me, and he appointed me as the class monitor. He told me what my duties in class would be and that I must make sure I came first in class work, tests and examinations. That last part encouraged me to work very hard at school and at home as I would not like to lose that position. I almost lost it one time when I came second in an exam. The girl that took the first position had just two more marks than I. Our teacher overlooked it and still retained me as the class monitor. Since then, I have not joked with my studies."

"Well done again. Any regret so far?"

"Yes. As I am the oldest in the class, some stubborn and younger pupils often poke fun at me like calling me *Baba*[2] or saying 'Your mates are in senior classes'. This at times makes me sad."

"But that is not your fault though. And, to be late is better than never," Ikẹ, as a big sister, encouraged Tayọ and hugged him. Through all this discussion, Dupẹ looked at the two of them and thought of good and bad experiences one could encounter when one goes to school. She was praying silently that their uncle would come as quickly as possible to come and speak to their grandparents as Ikẹ had told her.

Initially, Ikẹ meant to spend up to two weeks with them but because of her promise to Dupẹ to meet their uncle on her education issue, she left at the end of the first week.

Uncle Ezekiel was surprised to see Ikẹ return earlier than expected. She explained to him why she needed to come back early and appealed to him to do whatever he could to see that Dupẹ started school that year. After Ikẹ had finished talking, her uncle could not believe that Dupẹ was not going to school.

"What is she doing at present?"

"Just going to the farm with our grandparents. I was told sister Dayọ has been married off without going to school or learning any trade. I'm afraid if you don't do something very soon sir, sister Dupẹ may go the same way."

"Did you ask Dupẹ if she was interested in going to school at her age?"

"Yes, uncle. I asked her that question specifically and she's keen to start school once the opportunity comes."

"That's good to hear. I will take it up from there. How is Tayọ doing, farming too?"

"No, uncle. He is a bit lucky as they don't have any qualms allowing boys to go to school. They make sure almost all the boys are sent to school. Their misgiving is about girls. He too started school a bit late but from what I gathered, the problem was the sharp division between our father and our grandparents about where exactly Tayọ would start school - in our father's village or our grandparents' village and who would be responsible for his education and so on. Reason prevailed at last. He started going to school from our grandparents' village and he's doing quite well at school. In fact, he is the class monitor."

"Thank God for that. He must be *Baba* in his class but it's still very okay because the end justifies the means. All could turn out for him to be 'the person who laughs last laughs best.'"

"It's as if you were there, uncle. That's what his mates call him, *Baba*."

The following weekend, Ezekiel visited Tayọ's father. He enlightened him on the importance of education for all children regardless of their gender. After much debate, Tayọ's father agreed to let Dupẹ go to school on one condition. The condition was that he would not spend any money on her education. Ikẹ's uncle told him not to worry about that. He felt happy because the first obstacle had been removed. The following day, he went to Ọmọyẹ's village. After a warm reception, he called the grandparents and Dupẹ into a room and explained to them the purpose for his visit. After all the explanation, both grandparents kicked against the suggestion that Dupẹ should go to school at her age. They said they were already finding a good suitor for her in an arranged marriage which was the order of the day at that time. To them, allowing Dupẹ to go to school at that time was just a way to punish her grandmother whom Dupẹ was serving and keeping company with dutifully. They could not fathom the advantage of her going to school. On his way home, Dupẹ sadly saw her uncle off. He told her that by God's grace she would start school that year. That gave Dupẹ some comfort.

Ezekiel was not happy when he got back home that day. He
called his wife and Ikẹ together and told them what Dupẹ's
grandparents said. His wife who had warned him on such a
fruitless move said,

"Why do you always allow other people's problems to
overshadow your own? Now, they will be saying
everywhere that you want to cause confusion between Ikẹ's
father and his in-laws again. Please, be careful."

Ezekiel, in a pensive mood, nodded his head, looked
straight into his wife's eyes and responded thus, "You're
partially right. Some will reason like that. But what I want
you to know is this, 'All natural goods are bound to perish.
Riches take wings; fame is breath; love is a cheat. The most
enduring reality of all times is man's reflexive service to his
mankind.' That quote came from an anonymous person in
one of the books I once read. What I am doing today is not
for the present time, the advantage would be seen later and
posterity would judge maybe I was wrong or right. I will go
ahead and do this again because what will turn out
favourable, often starts out with many challenges."

With that plausible argument he put forward, his wife
agreed with him and left. Ikẹ hesitated a little bit but later
asked her uncle,

"Since they have disagreed with your good gesture, how do
you want to go about it, sir?"

"Well, let us wait and see. Without procrastination, I will move out again next week," Ezekiel responded.

"Thank you, sir."

When he was alone, Ezekiel recollected how he had the little education he could boast of. His going to school was haphazard. His father refused to send any of his children to school because they would be of no use in his vast farmland if they went to school. During the colonial time one day, one white man visited their village and picked all of them that were of school age and got them registered in school straight away. Through an interpreter, he told their parents that they were starting school and that they would be living with him. None of the parents could argue with him as they feared imprisonment. He and other boys and girls started primary school and later went to modern school. When they finished, they started working, some as teachers in the local primary schools and some as secretaries. They looked and behaved differently and people gave them respect.

After some years in the teaching profession, he joined the railway corporation where he rose to the post of a supervisor. So, he always thought that, if the white man had not given them that 'compulsory and free education', he would not have become who he was in life. By that fact, he was always ready to help children who wanted to go to school.

The following week, Ezekiel visited Tayọ's school to see the headmaster. Though the school was on holiday, the headmaster was around making arrangements for the next session. After greetings were exchanged, he explained who he was, his mission to the school and asked the headmaster to enrol Dupẹ for the coming school session. He also advised the headmaster to visit Dupẹ's village and tell her guardians that failure to let their granddaughter start school would involve government taking some action against them. The headmaster was happy with that suggestion because it displeased him when parents refused to send their children to school voluntarily despite government's warning against that.

One day during the holiday, the headmaster in company with the church catechist went to Dupẹ's village. They called all the parents together for a brief meeting. They informed them that the government would not hesitate to prosecute any of them who failed to send their children to school at whatever age they might be.

The headmaster told all the villagers in a very polite way, "According to the government's new law, age should not be a barrier to getting a basic education."

They wrote down the names of those children who were to start school the next session. When it was Dupẹ's turn, her grandmother asked the two of them,

"Who is going to spend money on her to go to school? You or your government? I want to know."

"Mama, if that's your fear, there will be no problem with that," both the headmaster and the catechist said assuredly.

"Please, emmaster[3], don't ask her to get anything from us. We are not giving a penny for the rubbish *sukul*[4] that you want all our young women to attend.

"*Kani ọmọde si niwọn, mo fara mọ. Awọn eleyii ti balaga ati pe wọn ti nṣetan fun ile ọkọ,*[5]" grandmother said. Though she was not sure of the correct pronunciation of 'headmaster', she made herself heard. She said further, "I don't think what you are doing to us is good. Why should your government force us to obey them and you all the time? You're doing as if your government owns all our children. No, they don't. Our children belong to us. God gave them to us."

"Mama, please try to understand. We're not here to force you to send your children to school but to make you know the importance of education for all children. We will not ask you to bring any money Mama. That's a promise," they told her.

"*Even if you ask us, we will not give you. Always sukul, sukul as if going to your sukul is the only way to be rich in life,*" she murmured to herself. Both the headmaster and the catechist left the village wondering if what they did would bring the desired result or not.

When they got back to their house, Grandmother told her husband all that happened at the meeting which he refused to attend. He listened carefully and said,

"Sooner or later, they will take over everything we have by force unless we fight it out with them. But how many of us are ready to fight them? I will just wait and see."

Later, Grandmother sat Dupẹ down and abused her for being an ingrate child like her father. She said, "Why should this government, their headteacher and the catechist be causing problems for people? Is it by force that every child must go to *sukul*? Why didn't you open your mouth and tell them you didn't want to go to *sukul*? *Ọmọ buruku*[6] ." She talked and talked but Dupẹ did not say a word. For the rest of the day, Grandmother was full of thought about what happened. Again, when they were about to sleep, she asked Dupẹ,

"How many ears do you have Dupẹ?"

"Two Mama."

"Listen carefully, if the *emmaster*[7] comes back to this village before the new school term starts, you must tell him you're not ready to go to school. If you tell him yourself, their government will not take us to court as they've threatened. Will you do that?"

"Em…. em….Yes Mama." Dupẹ said.

Kọlapọ visited his in-laws after Dupẹ's enrolment problem was over and none of them discussed Dupẹ's issue. Her father told them he would leave for Ibadan to look for work. He informed them that peace had not returned to his house and that his means of livelihood was not guaranteed.

He promised to send money and other things Tayọ might
need in his school to them from the city. Tayọ was sad to
hear the bad news. If his father moved to the city as he
planned, Tayọ wondered how he would cope at school with
buying of school materials, uniform and paying school fees.
He cried when his father was going but he appealed to him
not to cry. He gave him some money to at least make him
happy and said, "Tayọ, my son, I love you but you are too
young to understand what I am going through. I know God
will help you in life and you will become a well-known
doctor or lawyer. You will not live this type of life I'm
living. There are so many problems I am facing at present.
Don't worry, I will be coming to see you here and in your
school. But make sure you work hard and pass all your
exams." Tayọ was downcast for the rest of the day despite all
his father's assurance.

Before the next school resumption day, nearly all the people
in their neighbourhood had heard that Dupẹ was starting
school. Many were surprised while some congratulated her.
Her uncle visited the headmaster again and he was
informed that everything was in order for Dupẹ to start
school. The headmaster told him that Dupẹ would start
from primary three considering her age and knowledge.
Ezekiel thanked the headmaster for all he and the catechist
did to make Dupẹ's dream come true. Ezekiel bought all the
books, school uniform, bags and other school needs for her
as he promised. She was happy and thanked her uncle. He
advised her to be serious with her studies and that she

would soon finish her primary education since she would start from primary three. He gave her some money for her day-to-day school upkeep.

In the early morning of resumption day, Dupẹ woke up very early, took her bath and dressed up. She joined other children on their way to school. She was in no doubt, the oldest pupil among them. All the children called her 'aunty'. When they got to school surprisingly, Dupẹ met few other girls of her age whose parents had earlier refused to send to school at the right time. Unknown to her, the headteacher's and the catechist's visits to all the villages and her own story had caused a sort of 'big girls' revolution' in their area. She was happy she would not be the only big girl in the school.

The headmaster called the 'Committee of Big Girls' into his roomy office after the assembly was over. He told them not to feel bad that they were starting school late. He said it was possible later in life they could do far better than all the younger pupils that were their seniors in the school. His advice, "Don't count yourself too old. Education is a continuous thing without age limit. This is the most important aspect of any education. It is like a foundation of a house. This is why it is called 'primary'. Anything 'primary' is the most important and the basic. Listen to your teachers, ask your teachers questions on anything you do not understand. Study hard at school and home."

He told them the reason the school was placing all of them in primary three. The 'Big Girls' felt very happy with the pieces of advice and encouragement the headmaster gave them. They quickly formed a clique and did things in common.

With the headmaster's words of encouragement ringing in their heads, they all did well in their class work and behaved well. During the first term examination, Dupẹ came second. Grandmother's attitude towards her became hostile because she was feeling the impact of going to farm and doing housework all alone during the school term. Dupẹ did not allow Grandmother's attitude to worry her as much because of the inside joy she was having – joy of going to school at last. Tayọ also was doing well in his studies and he got promoted to primary five.

CHAPTER THREE

W*hile there's life, there's hope* - Marcus Tuttilius
Cicero

One weekend, a palm oil trader from Oluọdẹ
village came to Grandmother's house and told her that she
came across Ọmọyẹ on one of her trading trips to Ibadan.
Tayọ's grandmother could not believe it. She was very
happy to hear the good news about her 'lost' only daughter.
Her clapping and singing attracted other villagers who
trouped into her house. The woman who brought the good
tiding was the one who explained the source of the old
woman's joy to the people. She told them that Mama's 'lost'
daughter even took her down to the village where she lived.
She had re-married and she appeared to be doing well.

"It was by luck I came across her. I travelled to Ibadan and I
was looking for barrels of palm oil to buy which I always
resell. The palm oil market that day was very rowdy and I

was very tired at one point. As I sat down to have something to eat, behold, in front of me was Mama's daughter – Ọmọyẹ. She wanted to buy some of my palm oil. I looked at her carefully and knew for sure she was Ọmọyẹ. I called out her name, she looked at me and we hugged each other. We sat down and talked at length on so many things. She could not give me any tangible reason why she had not bothered to come and see her family here. She told me she would tell me the secret one day," the woman narrated her market meeting with Ọmọyẹ to everyone.

"My daughter, you said you saw Ọmọyẹ with your two eyes?" grandmother unbelievingly asked the woman again. The woman nodded in response.

"You said you talked on many issues. You said she is hale and hearty. My ancestors, I thank you. Long time ago, I was told she would come home one day. Our oracles never lie. Has she given birth to children? Did you see all of them? Oh, my ancestors in heaven, thank you all, I know you are not sleeping where you are. You have done me good. *Ewo lao niyọ si, ba ti fẹ o ri bẹẹ na lori, ewo lao niyọ si?*[1] " she sang in her native language - Yorùbá - and danced to her own music.

Many in the village rejoiced with her except those who had used her only daughter's disappearance to mock her and her grandchildren. However, those who had abused her and called her a witch because her only daughter ran away still came to hear the good news. Before the woman left, she told Grandmother the name of the village again and how people could get there if they wanted to go and see her. She assured her that her daughter, Ọmọyẹ, promised to visit very soon. When her husband returned from the farm, she did not let him have any rest before she broke the good news to him.

"Baba, at last, our 'lost' daughter, Ọmọyẹ, has been found," grandmother said.

"Ọmọyẹ, our daughter has been found? Who found her and where? Are you sure of what you are telling me?" he asked.

"*Bẹẹni,*[2] Baba Ọmọyẹ," she said with pride.

"How did this happen?"

"A certain woman from Oluọdẹ village came here few hours ago and told me and everybody in the village how she came across Ọmọyẹ during one of her trade journeys to Ibadan where she bought and sold palm oil. She said Ọmọyẹ even took her to the village where she is living with her new husband. She informed us that she promised to come and visit us anytime from now."

After her explanation, her husband said, "Hum….That is good. So, what that *Ifá* priest told us many years ago that Ọmọyẹ was still alive is true! My ancestors, thank you for this piece of information which we have been waiting to hear all these years."

Ọmọyẹ was everything to her mother. Before she was born, the old woman had given birth to more than four children but they all died at infancy. Ọmọyẹ's mother was never a

fatalist so she believed that her children's death was the
handiwork of her enemies and not from the gods. She went
from one native doctor to another in search of remedy to
make her children stay alive. When she was carrying
Ọmọyẹ's pregnancy, she was told not to go out in the mid-
afternoon especially if it was sunny and, not to go to any
funeral ceremony. She adhered strictly to the instructions
so as to be called a mother of a living child.

When Ọmọyẹ was born, many people including her parents
were still pessimistic about her survival. When she was four
years old, her mother gave birth to another baby boy. Her
joy was full. Many rituals were performed on her behalf as
revealed and directed by soothsayers to make the two
children live. Both children were pampered. They were
given whatever they asked for which were within their
parents' means and were loved by all their mother's friends.
People expected they would die but they did not. Ọmọyẹ
and her brother were inseparable. Ọmọyẹ loved him dearly
and never allowed him to be bullied by other children when
he was young. At the age of twenty-one, Ọmọyẹ was
married off to Tayọ's father amidst pomp and ceremony.
She never attended school or learned any trade. Kọlapọ, her
husband at that time was a very rich man and a man of
noble character. He showered her with love and money.
When Ọmọyẹ gave birth to her fourth child, her mother was
very happy that what she could not do by giving birth to
many children as she wanted, her daughter was doing.

She said to herself one day, *"Enemies thought I won't have many children but my ancestors have put all of them to shame. Some wives who gave birth to six, ten, eight or more children kept on abusing me. Now, Ọmọyẹ has given birth to four and I know she will give birth to eight or more children. I'm glad my ancestors have done this for me because all of her children will still be called my children. I pray my son will marry many wives and give birth to many children. That will shut the enemies' mouth up. Oluwa mi, ẹ seun o.*[3]*"*

Ọmọyẹ's younger brother grew up and he was getting ready to get married to his first wife which his anxious mother had been telling him to do all along. The date was fixed and the parents were fully prepared to make the day a memorable one. A few days before the wedding, the groom-to-be went to the farm as usual to tap wine for himself and his immediate family. He went in company with another friend. He was on top of a tall palm tree when the climbing rope he was resting upon snapped. He fell head down and died. When the incident was reported at the village, pandemonium took over the village and its surroundings. If tears could bring back the dead, his would have been the first to happen. His mother nearly died but she was consoled on the premise that Ọmọyẹ was still alive to take care of her. From that time, Ọmọyẹ remained the only living child of her mother.

"The world isn't fair, why would my brother just die like this? Could somebody have caused his death? I know God couldn't have taken him away from us at the prime of his life but.... em.... How

will I live peacefully without him? It's like half of me is dead, but who will understand? Could it be one of my stepmothers who killed my brother? Oh no.... I need to find out who did this evil to us one day. I must know who killed my lovely brother."

Ọmọyẹ who was present to console her mother sat down quietly one day and thought to herself when she remembered that her mother had had a quarrel with her father's last wife prior to that tragic incident. The junior wife threatened that she would deal with her and that Ọmọyẹ's mother would cry bitterly over her children. Because of that threat, Ọmọyẹ held the junior wife responsible for her younger brother's death though other people did not see it that way. She paid her mother a visit every week from her husband's village as one of the conditions given to her husband after her younger brother's sudden death. They knew her mother would need her closeness more than ever before. What nobody was able to decipher later was how Ọmọyẹ, just because of matrimonial problems, left her husband, her mother and her children for such a long time without considering the plight of the old woman who so much relied on her for companionship.

But contrary to people's expectation that day when she got the news of her daughter's whereabouts that she would feel bad, Ọmọyẹ's mother was full of joy.

Dupẹ and Tayọ came back from school that day after the woman who brought good tidings to their grandmother had left. They ate their meal. Grandmother sat both her grandchildren down and told them that a woman came to their village that day and told them that she had met their mother and that she was doing well. According to her, she was hale and hearty and that she had promised to come and see them. Dupẹ was happy to hear the news but Tayọ was sad.

He started a conversation, "Dupẹ, if our mother comes, I will neither greet nor talk to her. In fact, it's like I don't want her to come. So, she is alive all this while and she allowed us and our grandmother to be subjected to ridicule by villagers all the time. I think she is wicked."

Dupẹ and Grandmother told Tayọ to keep quiet and be grateful that his mother would eventually come back and see all of them.

"Mama, em...em.... em....and you will greet my mother if she comes?"

"Yes, I will, certainly."

"I can't understand why you have to Mama."

"You are an evil small boy, what's your problem? She remains my child no matter what she does," grandmother said. "Your mother had gone for such a long time and you are not happy that she is found alive!"

She moved to beat Tayọ but he quickly ran out of the place. In annoyance, she vowed not to give Tayọ any dinner for that day. He recollected the shame his mother's behaviour had brought to him and he remained sad that others, especially his grandmother and sister, did not see it that way.

''Em....Em...how do they expect me to greet somebody I can't recognise at my age?' he asked himself still thinking about past events since his mother left them.

He was moved to tears, but he knew he would do what he had planned to do if his mother showed up at any time. Weeks after that incident, Grandmother and everybody expected Tayọ's mother to arrive one day but alas, she did not. Her delayed promised visit put the old woman in great expectation and agony. Though she hid this as much as possible, her desperation to see and embrace her only child still showed in her actions from that day she was told her daughter was alive.

In Kufi village, marriage was an important festive occasion. Marriageable adults would be married off by their parents in an arranged way. Normally, in their village like others around it, men were not given the chance to look for women of their choice to marry. There were two major ways in which a man could be engaged to a woman.

The girl's father might decide to give his daughter away in marriage to his friend's son or his friend himself. This happened if such a father had been in constant harmonious relationship with his friend for a long time. If a female child was born, her father could tell his friend on that day that his newly born daughter would be given in marriage to one of his friend's sons whenever she was ripe for marriage. The friend from that time would become an 'in-law' of the man and would be doing all that was expected from real in-laws. This might involve bringing food stuffs to the girl's parents, giving money to them and showing them respect as their would-be in-law.

Alternatively, a father might mandate his friends to get a good wife for his son who was eligible for marriage. The friend who eventually succeeded and got a would-be wife would be the middleman between the girl's and the man's parents. If the girl's parents agreed, the middleman would inform the man's parents. The man's parents from then onward would be communicating by sending gifts to the girl and her parents through the middleman. If the intermediary was a man of unclean character, he would hold back some of the things sent to the girl and her parents. That might not be found out by either of the two parties immediately.

One very vital rule that must be followed in either of the two ways of getting a wife was that the man and woman were forbidden from any form of interaction until the day of the marriage. At times, black and white pictures of the would-be couple did exchange hands.

Another important factor to be considered was the question
of virginity. If the woman was found to have been
deflowered before marriage, the message would be
communicated to the woman's parents metaphorically. The
shame would last forever if the marriage survived at all. A
marriage ceremony for a wealthy man's son might last a
whole week, two weeks or three weeks depending on how
rich the family were. People from near and far would come
to celebrate with the couple and their parents. They would
wine and dine for the whole period of the marriage
ceremony. For the young boys in the village where the
occasion was taking place, it was the best time to eat the
best food with plenty assorted meat once they had worked
very hard to make the ceremony a success. Their work
before the ceremony was to construct as many make-shift
tents with palm fronds and planks in strategic locations of
the village and collect as many loads of firewood as possible
from the forest. That was to make the seating arrangement
for the visitors easier and aid the cooking of food. Without
these important functions from the young boys and men, a
marriage ceremony would not go well as there were no
modern amenities to do it any other way.

The second wife of Tayọ's grandfather had some male
children. One time, one of them was getting married.
Grandfather's village became a Mecca of sorts for the great
number of well-wishers who thronged their village.
Grandfather's house was like a palace. It consisted of about
twenty rooms and living rooms. He shared all these with his

younger brothers and their many wives and children and their daughters-in-law. The house conveniently accommodated all of them including some extended family members who lived with them.

The bridegroom lived in Ibadan which was a vast city but returned to the village a week before the wedding. Everything was in place before his arrival since it was the groom's father who was responsible for providing most if not all of the wedding facilities. The bride was brought at night on the wedding day as was the custom. After all the rites associated with the wedding were over, the wife's relatives were accommodated in a very large room waiting to get the result of their daughter's first marriage test - to know whether she was a virgin or not. If she was not, her people would not be entertained in the same way they would be if she had not met a man before. They would go back to their village with shame.

Tayọ and other young boys slept in a living room beside the couple's room. In the silence of the dead night, Tayọ and other boys heard some noises from the couple which they were expecting after all.

"Please, please, I beg you, forgive me, please, I beg you in the name of my mother and father. I have never done this before. Please. Promise you will…." the wife was pleading silently. "No, please, not that…. but I have been told it is usually pa....in....ful." She started crying. By that time everybody had been woken up but nobody uttered a word

as they were all anticipating the final outcome which was
the main issue for that first night.

"That's good for her and her family members as they will
have a rest of mind and get an unforgettable entertainment,"
one of the boys said quietly.

"Why did you say that?" another boy asked.

"It is because the wife has not been wayward and that's
good for her and her family. That's why she's crying."

The following morning, everyone did as if they heard
nothing during the night but joy was written in the face of
the wife's family. The wife went from one room to another
to greet her new adopted family members. All of them
rejoiced with her for passing her first marital test. When she
saw the boys, she greeted, "My 'young husbands' good
morning to all of you?"

"Good morning. You're welcome," they greeted back.

She referred to the boys as her 'young husbands' because
their customs demanded that a newly married woman must
never call her husband's younger brothers and sisters by
their first names even if such younger ones are as young as
ten years old. It's 'my young husband' or *akowe*[4] or brother
so and so' for boys or 'my young mother in-law' or 'sister so
and so' for the girls. The first offence a new wife could
commit was to call her husband's younger ones by their
names like Dupẹ, Ikẹ or Tayọ. The elders in the village
would tell her that she had not been well trained and that

she must not be heard calling the young ones in the family by their names. Some wives had been sent away just because of lack of respect for her husband's younger ones and family. If any wife followed that instruction as most would always do, she would get much respect and support from all her in-laws. It's an unwritten code of conduct.

When they left her, one of the boys said, "As I was saying during the night, this new wife has been very upright and well-mannered. What happened between her and her husband when we overheard them was very important. It is because of a day and night like that that makes almost all our young women not to be promiscuous. It is the day and night of reckoning. If you also noted, she greeted everyone with respect. These two tests she has passed will endear her to all of us."

After a week, the marriage ceremony was over. All the well-wishers who came to the wedding left for their different destinations. Second week after the marriage, the husband left for Ibadan. The wife could not go with him immediately because he did not have a personal apartment big enough to house himself and his new wife. His father was not responsible to provide that accommodation for him and his new wife no matter how rich he was. After the husband had left for the city, the wife complained to her father-in-law that she could not sleep alone as it was fearful being alone all night for the first time in her life. Her father-in-law mandated Tayọ to keep the woman company every night till her husband would be visiting again and take her to Ibadan. Tayọ, because

he was shy, refused at first to do that. Grandfather and Tayọ
were discussing the issue again when the new wife walked in.
As earlier stated, she called all the young schoolboys in the
village *Akọwe*. When she entered her father-in-law's room, she
knelt and said, "Baba, could you please allow *Akọwe* Tayọ to
move to my room and keep me company as I have requested."

"Ireti, our new wife, that is exactly what I am telling him
now. Tayọ, as you have heard, you will be sleeping in her
room every night to keep her company until her husband
comes back to the village."

"Thank you very much Baba," the wife stood up and left.

That night, Tayọ moved to the woman's room. From that
day he agreed to keep her company, she was good to him.
People often referred to them as 'husband and wife' to tease
Tayọ especially. Whereas the new wife was always happy to
hear that, Tayọ always felt uneasy. She would wash Tayọ's
clothes and beg on his behalf if he offended either his
grandfather or any other family members. Both the wife
and Tayọ were always together once he arrived from school.

"Where is your wife, Tayọ?" Grandfather and other people
would ask when they wanted to poke fun at him.

"No, she isn't my wife. She's uncle Kẹhinde's wife," Tayọ
would say.

"You are sleeping in a woman's room every night and you
are saying she is not your wife," grandfather said one day.

"If that is the case, I am not going to her room again to sleep," he said. He was already sleeping in his grandfather's room that night when the woman came in. She woke Tayọ up and said, "Good evening Baba. *Akọwe*, I have been expecting you. Let's go." He stood up sleepily and followed her. He forgot his afternoon vow never to go and sleep in her room again.

Tayọ's first thirst for romance with a girl took place one eventful day. Not too far from Tayọ's village is a village called Kutayi. There were many young girls in the village who were also attending the same school with him. The village was a stone's throw from Tayọ's. The two villages were linked together by a narrow road. On any typical day during holidays or weekends, he and other young ones were often sent on errands to other villages many times either to buy cigarettes, biscuits, kola, palm wine or some other items for the elders in their village. On each errand, he often met and played with any of the girls that came his way at that particular time. Among those girls was one called Risi. She was a Muslim and in the same class with Tayọ. She was fair in complexion and pretty. Everybody including the teachers loved to play with her because she was jovial and well-mannered. She interacted well with Tayọ. At times, she gave him part of her food in order for her name not to appear in the list of noise makers which Tayọ, as the monitor, compiled. He assisted her in her class work if she asked him for such help.

On one of such errands, Tayọ met Risi and said, "Risi, you know you are beautiful. Will you like to marry me when we grow up?"

"You're not serious. Who will marry a *kiriyo*[5] like you?"

"You know you attend a *kiriyo* school but you cannot marry a *kiriyo* boy like me," Tayọ countered to defend his religion.

"That apart, my father will never allow me to marry anyone from your village. It's quite near."

"But we'll live in Ibadan City which is quite far from here and where there are modern infrastructural facilities like good roads, phone lines, electricity, water supply, hospitals, university, big markets, etc."

Risi did not respond. Tayọ continued, "I will go to university and you will become the wife of a medical doctor or a lawyer which my father has told me I would become one day."

"Don't you like that?" Tayọ asked.

"Let's wait and see," she replied.

One afternoon during the second term holiday, Tayọ was sent to Risi's village to buy something. He was happy to go because that was another opportunity to see Risi. He passed through her house but nobody was around. That saddened him. On his way back home, Risi appeared from a bush path that joined a narrow road. She was alone. They exchanged greetings and started to talk as usual right in the middle of the road.

"I passed through your house few minutes ago," Tayọ said opening the discussion.

"Did you see anyone," Risi asked unconcernedly.

"No,' Tayọ said. "Where are you coming from?"

"Nowhere in particular, I was just asked to go and bring some fresh pepper and vegetable from our nearby farm," she said.

"If you won't mind, may I pluck some oranges for you from that orange tree; will you come with me?" Tayọ pointed to ripe oranges beside the road.

"I don't like oranges much."

"Ok, let's go there."

"But what for?"

"Nothing but em...em...let's just leave this place."

Risi wanted to run straight home but Tayọ held her hands and begged her to just follow him. After much pressure, she agreed to go with him. They entered the bush but unknown to them, one man was on one of the kola trees that surrounded the place. The man kept quiet and watched what they were up to.

"Let's play," Tayọ still unsure of the next thing to do said, looking straight into her beautiful eyes.

"How do we play?" she asked.

"We will remove our...." Tayọ responded.

"No, we can't do that. Our parents have warned us never to do things like this."

"I know. You're right but don't worry. They won't see us and they won't know. Nothing will happen to you." They slowly started to take off their dress. The man kept quiet. He was surprised at what the two children were up to. Halfway as they continued to undress, he walked up to them. When they both saw him, they were shaking and speechless. The man was from Táyò's village. Tayọ wanted to bolt. He took few steps.

The man shouted at him, "If you run Tayọ, I will catch and give you the beating of your life. Come back here now."

He stopped immediately. Fearing the man might carry out his threat to deal with him, he came back. Both Tayọ and Risi started to cry.

"Sorry Baba, we're just playing," Risi said.

"Is this what you call play?"

"No. No. em.... em.... but...." Tayọ did not know what to say.

"Now, both of you, wear your clothes properly and tell me what you are trying to do here. I want to know."

"I told him that our parents must not see us or hear about this but…." Risi said with shaking voice.

"Hear about what?" the man asked.

"Sorry Daddy, I…. I…. I…. told him sir…. that…."

"That he should bring you here?"

"No sir, no….no…. no. That we should go home," Risi said.

"Is this the place where the two of you were sent to?" the man asked.

"Please daddy, we are not trying to do anything, but we will not do this…. Please sir, don't tell people, beat us now. I beg you. We will do whatever you ask us to do sir," Tayọ pleaded.

With uncoordinated phrases and sentences, Tayọ and Risi continued to beg the man for forgiveness. The man at a point laughed at their comic behaviour. Both of them knew that, if they were reported to their parents, they would be beaten and shamed.

"How many ears do you have?"

"Two sir," both chorused.

"Go straight home. You must not try any silly thing like this again. Next time, if I or any other person see you doing this,

I will march you to the village naked for everyone to see what both of you are up to," the man told them. Before he allowed them to go, he cut a cane and gave each of them six strokes as punishment for their wrongdoing. None of them cried, even Tayọ who dreaded cane received his strokes of cane with joy.

"Listen. As from today, don't let me see you together. I will ask other children to watch you in your school and everywhere. If you are seen together again, I will make sure I tell your parents about this but if you keep to my warning, no one will hear anything. Is that right?" the man asked.

"Yes sir. Thank you, Daddy. You will not see us together again. We are sorry sir."

They called the man 'Daddy and *Baba*' because any man or woman who was not somebody's biological parent but who was old enough to be, was often referred to by the younger ones as 'Daddy or Father or Baba' or 'Mummy or Mother or Mama' in their tradition.

Tayọ prostrated while Risi knelt to thank the man for his promise to cover their shameful act.

"You can go to the village or wherever you were sent."

They both quickly went away with fear of what might happen next. When Tayọ got back to the village, he did not meet the man who sent him on an errand and luckily for him, the item he went to buy was not damaged. He gave them to the man's wife. Throughout the rest of the day, he was chilled to the marrow and kept himself indoor. His first amorous contact with the opposite sex was a disaster.

It was a tradition in Tayọ's village for elderly men and women from each household to go out every morning to greet all other villagers before they would leave for the farm or market. The man who caught Tayọ and Risi in the act was coming to greet Tayọ's grandparents the following day. Tayọ, Dupẹ, and their grandmother were eating together at the passage of their house when the man appeared. Swiftly, Tayọ stood up and ran into the room. The man did not see him taking to his heel. After he had greeted everybody, he asked, "Where is Tayọ?" When Tayọ heard that, he wished the ground could open up and swallow him. He was frightened to the marrow by the man's innocuous question.

"He ran into the room just now. Has he done something wrong to you?" Tayọ's grandmother asked out of curiousity.

"No, Mama. Greet him for me," he said. When he heard that from him, he felt relieved. After all, he knew he was not in their house to report him. He resurfaced after he had gone. He was asked by his sister why he ran away from the man. He told her that he beat the man's child the previous week and that was why he had been running away from him ever since. Tayọ respected the man for keeping what happened as a secret as he promised.

After that episode, if he was sent to Risi's village, it was as if he was sent to a gas-oven to be killed. Something often reminded him of that incident and the man's cautioning.

Also, any time either he or Risi saw the man, each would
run back to where they were coming from or hide
somewhere to avoid meeting him. Nobody understood why
they always did that.

At school, Tayọ and Risi stopped talking to each other as the
man instructed. If they met on the road, they would just go
by without any interaction whatsoever. Their behaviour
surprised people who knew how intimate they used to be.
Nobody knew the source of their sudden change in
behaviour and none of them said anything about what
happened.

CHAPTER FOUR

I nitiative is doing the right thing without being told -
Victor Hugo

Ọmọyẹ did not come as she promised though many
months had passed. No message was received from her
either. Her mother became so worried and confused. One
day during the holidays, Grandmother gave Dupẹ transport
fare and asked her to go and check if it was true that her
mother was living in that village where the woman said she
went to see her. Dupẹ was very happy to go. She promised
that if she met her mother, she would spend up to a week
with her.

In the evening of the third day of her departure, Dupẹ
arrived back to the village. Grandmother was surprised to
see her so early. Dupẹ was asked about what happened. She
narrated her bitter experience,

"When I got to my mother's village after so much trouble because of the bad road, I met her and she gave me a cold welcome. Mama, you will not believe this, it pained me. You would think that after such a long time since we last saw each other, I would receive a better welcome. Why she did that to me, I don't understand."

Grandmother having listened to Dupẹ patiently said, "You saw Ọmọyẹ, my daughter? You're sure you saw her?"

"Yes Mama. Will I be lying about this?"

"But I told you not to go. That's good for you. You and Mama were not happy with what I said the other day," Tayọ who was there when she was narrating her experience said.

Dupẹ acted as if she did not hear him and continued, "When I got there, I was fortunate I saw my mother first. The first statement she uttered was, 'Who sent for you? I ask, who sent you here?' In fact, I felt very ashamed. I told her you sent me and she was not moved. I decided to return that day but her husband begged me to stay. He reprimanded her for behaving to me the way she did."

"Dupẹ, how many children has she given birth to?" grandmother asked.

"I don't know Mama, but she has got some children."

"I thank my father in heaven for blessing her with more children," grandmother said.

Tayọ went out at once when Grandmother asked that question about how many children their mother had got. He muttered to himself, *"But, why does our grandma always love a woman to have many children when the woman may not be able to take proper care of such children? Hers is always, more, more and more children."*

Grandmother appealed to Dupẹ not to be offended. She told her that the joy of it was that Ọmọyẹ, their mother, was still alive. She promised to go there personally and see her if she failed to come to the village.

One day, Tayọ's grandfather suddenly died. Tayọ had heard of deaths of many people he knew around their locality, but no one very close to him had died. If a person died and Tayọ knew him or her, it would take a long time before he would be able to pass by the person's home, burial ground or farm area. He believed the dead person could still appear to him. That was because his grandfather had often told stories of how in the past, he had met one deceased person or the other face-to-face.

One of such stories that he could never forget was narrated to them one day by Grandfather during a moonlight storytelling. He said he was going to another village one sunny afternoon when he met one of his friends who he did not know had died that morning. Grandfather said they sat down on the road and talked on many issues. The dead man told Grandfather where he was going and for how long he would be away. He sent a message to his family through Grandfather which he said he had forgotten to tell them when he left them that morning.

He gave Grandfather the names of his creditors and debtors and the amounts involved. The old man, armed with the message, went to the man's village. The first man he met as he was entering the village informed him that the same man who had given him a message to deliver to his family members died that morning. Not until he saw the dead man's body did he believe he had died. A few days after the man's funeral, he went back to visit the deceased family and explained to them how he had met their father on his way that morning not knowing he was already dead. They were surprised beyond imagination because, some of them knew about the money issues in the message he sent to them. Since Grandfather told them that fearful story, Tayọ was always terrified each time a person he knew died. He often imagined his grandfather's weird experience would happen to him and wondered how he would act.

The day preceding his death, Grandfather was hale and hearty. Tayọ went to the farm with him. They came back in the afternoon hoping to go for the evening session. Towards the evening time, he told Tayọ he would like to have some rest. He therefore sent him alone to the farm to bring some tubers of yam which they did not bring with them that afternoon. The farm was about twelve miles round trip. Initially Tayọ did not want to go but when he remembered some past beatings from his grandfather, he sadly left for the farm.

What baffled him most was that he did not meet anyone on his way to the farm. That was quite unusual because there were many villages on the way and they always met many people on their way to and from each time they went to that farm. After a long trek, he got to the farm. He collected four big tubers of yam as his grandfather had directed. He was looking for a strong rope to tie them together when he heard a man's voice greeting him.

"Tayọ, how are you today?"

"Who is that? Who is greeting me? Please, who has called my name?" he asked but no one answered. He looked front, back, right, left and up the trees. He saw no one. He quickly tied the tubers of yam and tried to lift them onto his head. He looked back, front, left and right again, there was nobody. He shouted and asked, "Who greeted me just now?" Again, nobody answered. He was afraid as he was sure he heard a man's voice. He became nervous. Hurriedly, he lifted the tubers of yams onto his head and left in haste. The recollection of fearful stories he had been told worsened the situation for him. Birds' chirps became the living noise he could hear. He kept on going with the belief that he would soon see somebody. No one surfaced. He started singing aloud to drive out his fear. The fear persisted. The sun had set before he got back home. He told his grandfather that he did not meet anyone on his way going to the farm and

coming back home and that, he was so afraid. He told him
how he thought he heard a greeting from a man whom he
did not see. He said all that so that his grandfather would
credit him for his courage. He was discouraged when his
grandfather said,

"Darkness catches up with a small boy in a forest. When he
comes back home, he tells the people that he is brave. If he
is not brave, would he have slept inside the forest? Tayọ, if
you were really afraid this evening, would you have slept in
our farm or on the road? You are a man, could you always
behave like a man?"

Tayọ understood the proverb and he felt sad that
Grandfather had not given him any credit for being brave.

That night, there was a heavy rain. Tayọ slept soundly and
woke up late. Hastily, he bathed, ate his food and dressed up
for school. He was on his way out of their house when
Grandfather called him back to come and fold his sleeping
mat. He quickly did that and left for school in company
with other pupils. They arrived school late. They were given
strokes of the cane by the headmaster for their lateness. The
school closed for the day and on their way back home, the
pupils were hearing shouting and wailing just some
distance from their village. They ran to the village and in
front of Tayọ's house were scores of people. Sympathisers
told the children that Tayọ's grandfather died just an hour
after they had left for school that morning. Tayọ threw his
school bag away and ran inside and asked,

"Whose grandfather died?"

"Your grandfather has died," a woman said.

Tayọ looked at his grandmother where she sat down crying and he too started crying. From that day, his belief that only people who were sick or have accidents that could die changed. His grandfather was not sick. He did the usual village greetings that morning and asked him to fold his mat and put it in the proper place before he left for school. Why and how he died shocked him.

As it was customary in their village, all the first children from Grandfather's wives had to be present before he could be buried. As a result, Ọmọyẹ, the first and the only surviving child of her mother must come for her father's burial. Tayọ would get a chance to set his eyes on his mother after so many years of her disappearance. She could not run away any more from her own shadow. She must respect their departed father and custom.

Emissaries were sent to inform all the man's children of his demise. What concerned Tayọ most was to meet a mother who had left her own children and parents for all those past years without looking back.

"What if she decides not to come? Well, she dares not," he was thinking hard on the possibility of his mother refusing to attend her father's burial. Before the evening time, the village was filled with people who had come to commiserate with the family.

The next day, people continued to arrive in the village. Ọmọyẹ, in company with her new husband and their relatives also arrived in the village. They cried and after their dirge which went on for some minutes, they went round the village to greet other people. Ọmọyẹ cried her eyes out for her late father whom she had not bothered to see for years. Everybody was surprised. Many kept aloof from her while some embraced her and her new-found family. The wailing gathered momentum. Immediately Tayọ heard of her arrival, he came out. He did not recognise her as he had once thought. He noted she must be the one wailing the most. To say that he was bitter seeing his mother weeping was an understatement. He neither moved near her nor ran away from her.

"So, this woman comes to bury the dead while she neglects the living all this while? Why couldn't she let the dead bury their dead? She knows she still has people she may mourn even in death while she does nothing for them when they are alive?" Tayọ asked himself those rhetorical questions.

When Ọmọyẹ came back, she went to where her aged mother sat, she knelt in front of her. They placated each other for their loss. Grandmother praised her for coming early for her father's burial. Tayọ watched the whole scene distastefully. Dupẹ was by her mother's side since she arrived which irritated Tayọ all the more. Maybe because of sacredness of blood between mother and child, his mother asked suddenly, "Mama, where is Tayọ?"

"He is the one behind you," grandmother said.

"Which one of these children?"

Many were not shocked that Ọmọyẹ could not recognise her own child. They just saw how wicked she was for staying away from her family all those years since Tayọ was a baby. However, it appeared she was not humbled. Dupẹ pointed directly to Tayọ. His mother beckoned to him to come. Instead of answering her call, he ran out of the house. Whereas some people said he was childish for not welcoming his runaway mum, he thought otherwise. He avoided her as much as possible for the first two days of her arrival.

The next morning when the meeting on how the funeral event would go was held, Ọmọyẹ was asked by one of her older stepbrothers why she left for all those years and refused to come and see the children and her own family including her aged mum. She was angry but she gave some silly reasons for her aloofness and devil-may-care attitude.

That day, she sent Tayọ on an errand but he refused to go. "You are useless from birth; I know that. You will continue to suffer if you continue this way," Tayọ's mother said. Instead of saying anything, he left her. Ọmọyẹ asked her mother if Tayọ's father had come since her father died. The woman said 'no'.

"He is a wicked man. I know. Didn't I tell all of you? You can see it clearly. My father who took care of his children is dead but he couldn't even come and pay him his last respects."

Tayọ just laughed and said to himself, *"Ho! Who is more wicked? She's just a pot calling the kettle black. I think my father is far better. I don't think he could ever run away from us."*

During the funeral, many cows, which were bought on credit by some of Grandfather's children and family, were slaughtered. Guests from other villages and cities came and ate for days celebrating the worthy life which Grandfather lived including people, who never came to say hello to him when he was alive. Ọmọyẹ, her step brothers and sisters with their family left after the befitting burial rites were completed.

His death did not do much harm to Tayọ's life because the man was neither responsible for his schooling nor feeding in any proper sense. The man left his wives to take care of their respective children and grandchildren. Occasionally however, he often asked them to come to his farm and get some baskets of cassava, maize and yam tubers. The day-to-day feeding rested solely on the ability of the wives to work hard and cope. Since Tayọ came to that village, the man never bought a yard of cloth for him not to mention a pair of shoes. Grandfather, in essence, did not contribute much to his daily living.

All the same, Tayọ regretted his sudden death as he would not be able to attend their church's Elders' meeting which was on rotational basis. At each elder's turn to hold the meeting, the host would provide food and drinks in excess for the members. The meeting always took place after the church service every last Sunday of each month. Tayọ was their official 'secretary' during each meeting. He was the oldest of the children who always accompanied their fathers and grandfathers to the meeting and he could write and read in Yorùbá fluently. Tayọ, as their secretary, was often given special portions of food and meat as the elders valued him so much for the accuracy of the minutes of the meeting that he always took and read to them no matter how long back in time the meeting had taken place. During each meeting, he would take the attendance, record absences, tell them how much was in the account, amount contributed that day, how much money had been spent for church activities or as gift to members during child naming, housewarming or funeral of dead parents. It was also his duty to inform them who would host the next meeting and when. All the elders always informed the women preparing the meeting meals to give their secretary a special portion. Tayọ was always looking forward to such meetings and the special recognition he would be given. But suddenly, his grandfather had passed on and would no more be attending the meeting. That ended his own attendance and coveted position and recognition.

Prefects' appointment often took place at the end of the third term of each academic year in Tayọ's school. They

were always chosen among the incoming primary six
pupils. He and some few other pupils were doing well
academically right from primary one. All the pupils
were wondering who their school would choose as
prefects among them. Though all teachers and the
headmaster would have known who the appointed
prefects were, they were never allowed to divulge the
information so as to intensify the suspense that came
with it and give the posts some credibility and aura. On
the last day of the session, the assembly was full. Pupils
sang joyfully and all looked anticipatory. After the
morning devotion, the headmaster advised pupils to
make sure they helped their parents during the long
holiday and never forget to prepare fully for the coming
school term. He also advised them to remind their
parents of their school fees, books for their new classes
and school uniforms. Though all those were important,
all the pupils waited with bated breath for the most
crucial news of the day, the calling out of names of all
the new prefects.

"Now, it is time for me to call out the names of the new
school prefects. It has taken the school much time to
consider who among you in primary 5, on your way to
primary 6, that will be our prefects. You are all very
intelligent, hardworking and reliable. Not all the time do we
have these qualities in our students. We thanked all our
outgoing prefects for their wonderful performance,
academically and morally. We pray that you will continue to

excel wherever you find yourselves in life. Can all of you say 'Amen' to that?"

"Aaaamen," all pupils said.

"Getting to this stage in life is far-reaching. And for one to be considered for any school post is a worthy and life-long experience. We believe any time you remember today in years to come, you will be proud of yourself. Don't see yourself as better than many that have not been chosen. See yourself as someone who has distinguished himself/herself from an honourable crowd. As such, you have to show leadership qualities all the time. There have been few cases where some prefects have been relieved of their posts. Please, do not join the number."

As you all know, this set of pupils are next in rank to the teachers in the school administration. With that in mind, all of you must show them respect and support," the headmaster continued choosing his words very carefully and slowly. To all the pupils however, it was as if the announcement would never be made.

"When I call each of your names, please come out. As they come out, could all of you give them a round of applause. In the absence of nothing else, our school's new head prefect is........" the headmaster stopped suddenly and motioned his assistant to check something in the file containing the list he was holding. Without any apology he resumed, "The new head prefect for the next academic session for this school is Ọmọtayọ Sam Kọlapọ."

Tayọ came out. The headmaster, his assistant and all teachers shook hands with him. He was all smiles. Other prefects were called out one after the other. Ironically, the head girl was Risi. What a coincidence. Though separated since that ugly romance incident in the bush, they were joined by their new school posts.

Tayọ got home and told his grandmother that he had been chosen as the new head boy of his school. His grandmother was very happy. From that time on, she told everybody about it. He and his grandmother became well known in their locality. Wherever they went, other pupils would be telling their parents about Tayọ being their school new head prefect. Some would come and congratulate the two of them and wish his grandmother long life to reap the fruit of all her labour for her grandchildren.

Schools resumed for the new school session and Tayọ was in primary six. He attended school punctually, became more obedient, maintained his excellent academic record and led by example. At times, if the headmaster and other teachers arrived school late on Monday from Ibadan where they spent their weekends, Tayọ and other prefects would conduct the morning assembly peacefully. This endeared them more to the school staff. By doing that, he was involved in the school's administration at that young age.

One morning when the school assembly was still proceeding, Dunni's father came to the school with a very sharp cutlass. He was tall, sturdy and his menacing attitude made him look like a wounded lion. His daughter, Dunni, noticed him first. She immediately ran away from the assembly and once other teachers and pupils saw him coming, they all dispersed like wind, leaving just the headmaster to face the very agitated man.

Some girls in Dupẹ's class were mature as they started school very late. Their ages ranged from 15 to early 20s. Dunni was one of the girls. She was pretty and brilliant. Mr Owonifaari always asked her to come to his room after the school had closed to help him with cooking which was a normal thing for girls to do for their unmarried male teachers. As such, nobody suspected the teacher was having a secret affair with her. She began to sleep in the class. This led her class teacher to report her to the headmaster who found out the truth. After much pressure, one of her friends she had confided in told the headmaster what happened. She was expecting. He tried to find out who was responsible for the pregnancy but he did not succeed. When her parents noticed her changed behaviour and body shape, her father threatened to kill her for bringing shame to his family. She was pressured to reveal the culprit. It was her teacher, Mr Owonifaari. The revelation shocked her parents. She was warned to keep the information to herself.

"*Hem-masta*[1], where is *misita*[2] Owonifaari?" the man asked the bewildered headmaster as he raised his cutlass.

"Please Baba, he is em...em...em...em....," the headmaster was saying as he was taking some steps backwards.

"*Hem-masta* if you move again....em....em....em blood will flow now," he lowered his cutlass and rushed at the headmaster.

"Sorry, sorry, sorry Baba, that is Mr Owonifaari," he pointed to the offender who was already quite far away from the two of them. Once he saw the headmaster pointing in his direction, he ran as fast as his feet could carry him breathing like a marathoner. Like lightning, he entered primary six classroom and jumped out from there through one of the windows right into the jungle. Dùnní's father ran after him but he was no match to catch him. He shook his head as if he had lost a hunted prey. He furiously came back to the school but met no one. He was talking to himself as he left the school,

"*God save that shameless teacher today. If I had caught up with him, he would be swimming in his own blood by now. The case has not ended here.*" Suspense enveloped the school.

When the headmaster was certain that Dunni's father had left for his village, he asked the school timekeeper to ring the bell for another assembly but by that time, many pupils were too scared to come out of their hiding. While the teachers were looking for their pupils all over the place, the headteacher made his apologies for what had happened. He told all those who managed to come back to the school that they must come to school the next day as usual. He assured all of them that the ugly incident would never happen again. He told them that the school, with the cooperation of the

church, village chiefs and parents would find amicable
solution to the problem. He dismissed the pupils. For the
rest of that day, nothing much was done. But Mr
Owonifaari was missing.

It was the next day at school that most pupils heard what
happened to Mr Owonifaari after he had jumped out
through the window during the fracas. He was not familiar
with the village tick forest area. As he was running away
from an imminent death from the hand of Dunni's father,
he stepped on a snare placed to catch animals by a hunter.
His right leg was battered. In pain he shouted for help but
there was no immediate help coming from anywhere.
Before any human help could come, a hunting dog got to
where he was and started biting him. As he could not move
out of the snare and escape, he fought the dog with the last
strength left in him. The dog owner who was tracing where
his dog was howling came face to face with Mr Owonifaari,
almost dying and incoherent. He was surprised. He chased
his dog away and set Mr Owonifaari free. He was bleeding
from his wound. He carried him on his shoulder to the
village with great hardship. When the villagers noticed that
Mr Owonifaari had become unconscious, they started
shouting, "Teacher must not die. Teacher must not die. If
teacher dies, his government that posted him to this school
will surely kill all of us." They did everything possible to
resuscitate him. There was no hospital near the village
school to take him to for immediate treatment. Village
traditional health dispensers were called upon and they

tried to save his life. At last, he came round and all the villagers were happy. When Dunni's father heard what happened to the seducer, he ran away from his village. He realised he might be held responsible for whatever happened to the embattled teacher notwithstanding the fact that he was the one that caused all the problem in the first instance. He remembered the popular saying in his locality that *Agbefọba kan kii jẹbi.*[3] Nobody knew the whereabouts of Dunni for the rest of that day.

Mr Owonifaari left the village for the city where he was able to receive proper treatment in the hospital. After some months, he came back to the village to resume work. While some villagers sympathised with him, many regarded him as a sex pest. They thought that if government was always fair to their citizens as they always claimed, Mr Owonifaari should have been dismissed as a teacher or sent to another faraway school for the crime he committed.

After a series of village meetings with the school representatives, the church and Dunni's parents, the teacher was forced to marry her as they were not interested in any other option. He was told what and what to bring to pacify Dunni's parents and family as their custom demanded. He fully complied. The shame was too much for the Romeo. He left the school unceremoniously with his new wife. The incident led to mass withdrawal of many mature female pupils from the school and this gave the school a bad image.

CHAPTER FIVE

C arry out a random act of kindness, with no expectation of reward, safe in the knowledge that one day someone might do the same for you - Princess Diana

During the annual Children Harvest's Day celebration at Tayọ's church, it was the usual thing for the church catechist in conjunction with the headteacher to ask the school head prefect boy or head prefect girl to read the only Bible lesson for that important day. Whether the head boy or head girl was a Muslim or Christian was immaterial. Muslim parents saw nothing wrong in their children doing that as they believed all of them were worshipping the same God. At the same time, they took it as an honour to their child. The lesson was always read in Yoruba Language, their mother tongue. Tayọ, as the head boy was chosen to read the lesson that year. He told his father few weeks before that day to buy him new clothes and a pair of shoes and to come to church from Ibadan for the event. He wanted him and his grandmother to sit in the front seat which the church often reserved as a mark of respect for the parents for producing a brilliant boy or girl who could face the audience and read to them. Unfortunately, his father only bought him new clothes but no shoes. To make matters worse, his father did not attend the church service. He was not happy that morning. His heart was pounding thinking on how he would face the congregation and read a Bible lesson without putting on any shoes. His grandmother cheered him up early that morning and they left for the church celebration.

When it was time for the Bible reading, the catechist announced, "The only Bible reading for today's Children's Harvest Day will now be read to us by our primary school head boy, Ọmọtayọ Sam Kọlapọ. Please, be very attentive. May the Lord bless His words and make all of us the doers of His words and not hearers alone."

The congregation said 'Amen.'

Tayọ moved out from the choir seat where he had been a member since he was in primary three. His grandmother was alone on the seat in front of the lectern where the Holy Bible he would read from was placed. As he was going out, tens of eyes were focussed on him. He walked boldly to the lectern and said,

"Good morning, sir. Good morning ma. Good morning pupils. Good morning, friends."

Then he continued the ritual, "The Bible lesson for today is taken from the book of Malachi Chapter 3." He remembered all that his headmaster and the catechist had taught him to do when he got to the lectern. He checked the back of the Bible where all the books in the Bible were listed. After he had checked for Malachi Chapter 3, easily, he opened to the chapter and commenced reading while many congregants were still looking for it. He did not look at the people. He read the verses with ease in Yorùbá. Once he finished, he said, "May God bless His word."

He went back to his seat as he was given a loud ovation. When he sat down, he felt like a coup plotter that had been set free. Where the boldness came from, he could not tell. On their way home, his grandmother said, "Tayọ, you are a very good boy. You did not allow what happened about your father's absence or lack of shoe to wear to the church disturb you. You have made me happy. *Ọlọrun mi a gbe ọ ga l'Orúkọ Jesu Kristi.*"[1]

"Amen Mama but I was really afraid this morning before you advised me not to worry."

"That's good of you. Whatever happens today is not the end of life. If you don't have a pair of shoes today, you will have many in the future."

"That's true Mama. Thank you."

The following school day, the headmaster called Tayọ. He told him that the catechist would want to see him after school hours. Tayọ became very apprehensive as most of such meetings between the catechist and pupils were not always positive. The school often referred serious acts of disobedience or any other problem from pupils to the catechist who would thereafter invite the parents of the offending pupils and discipline their child in their presence.

"Did I do anything wrong at the church yesterday? Am I in trouble? God, please help me today," he said to himself when he left the headteacher.

He went to see the catechist, Mr Kọmọlafẹ, as instructed. He knocked at the door and he was asked to come straight in.

"How are you today Tayọ? I hope you enjoyed school."

"I am fine sir. Yes, I did sir."

"How did you feel in Church yesterday?"

"I was afraid at first but I managed to do my best as my grandmother had told me yesterday morning that I should not worry. She assured me that everything would go well."

"That's very good of you. You read the Bible passage confidently despite the fact there were many people in attendance than in any of our ordinary Sunday service. You know what, I'm proud of you."

"Thank you very much sir," he said as he observed the meeting was positive.

"Samson," the catechist called on one of his children. He was Tayọ's age mate.

"Bring those three pairs of shoes here." Samson brought the shining shoes to him.

"Tayọ, try these three pairs of shoes on and let's see which one is your size. If any of them fits you, take it."

He was surprised. He did not know what was happening or whether he heard the catechist clearly. *"Did our catechist hear what Grandma said yesterday about this shoe issue to me? No, I don't think so. Am I dreaming? No, I'm not,"* he said to himself.

Just the previous day in church, he was not wearing a pair of shoes because he did not have one. But miraculously, he was being presented with a pair of shining shoes. He looked intently at the three pairs and timidly tried on the black shoe. It was as if it was specially made for him. Before he could say anything, the catechist and Samson said simultaneously, "Oh Tayọ, that's exactly your size."

"It looks very smart on you," Samson said further.

"I think so. It is very fine," the catechist said.

"Yes sir. Thank you, sir."

'Samson, bring one carrier bag for him so he could put the shoes in." Tayọ prostrated himself before the catechist and thanked him and Samson for the one in a lifetime gift.

"Sir, please may I say thank you to Mummy too?"

"Yes. Mummy, Tayọ wants to greet you," Mr Kọmọlafẹ called on his wife who everyone often referred to as 'Mummy'. She came and he prostrated himself before her and thanked her for the gift.

"Tayọ, that's all right. Samson, go into my room and bring the brown bag beside my bed. Tayọ, wait a minute." Samson brought the bag.

She collected the bag from Samson, opened it and said, "These trousers and shirts are for you. You are a good boy."

"Ha, thank you, Mummy. Thank you, Daddy. Thank you, Samson."

"You're welcome. I pray the Lord will bless you. You will go places in Jesus' Holy Name."

"Amen, ma."

"You don't need to tell people that we gave you all these items. Greet your grandmother and sister."

He left the catechist's home with great joy. He did not open the bags until he got back to his grandmother's room. Dupẹ, who wanted to know who he was meant to give the bags to did not get a clue from him.

"Come and see something," he called his grandmother and Dupẹ into the room when he got back home. He showed them the pair of shoes and the clothes. Both of them were very happy for the unexpected kindness from their catechist and his family.

"Mama, it was yesterday you told me that though I did not have a pair of shoes to wear to church, you said I would have many to wear in the future. You'll soon become a prophetess," Tayọ said.

"Ha…. ha…. ha…. (She laughs). My child, God works in miraculous ways. *Alaaanu ni Ọlọrun wa.*[2] When I said yesterday that you would have many shoes in future to wear, I did not know part of what I said would come true today. I have to go right now and thank the catechist and his family for this. When your father comes next time, I'll tell him to go and thank the catechist also," grandmother said.

"He must go and thank him and his family," Dupẹ and Tayọ said.

"But Mama, you can thank the catechist next Sunday; it's getting late already," Dupẹ advised.

"It's necessary I do it now. Don't forget that our catechist often preached that we should show immediate appreciation for every good thing done for us, which I believe is very true," grandmother said as she left the village for their catechist's home.

Tayọ sat the common entrance examination into secondary school. Government College Ibadan (GCI) was one of the most popular secondary schools in Nigeria. It was a school where the children of the rich and famous people attended.

It was a go-to and well-known high school that had produced so many political and economic leaders for the country. But the entrance criteria were strict. The school gave scholarship to five indigent students who passed the common entrance test every year. The cut-off pass mark for that year when Tayọ sat the common entrance for GCI was 585 out of a total of 600. His primary school had chosen two very competitive grammar schools in the city for him where the children of the rich and educated people attended. They did that because they believed he would score very high mark that would get him an admission. When the result was released, Tayọ scored 575. So, going to GCI was out of the question. The cut-off mark for his second-choice school, Ibadan Boys High School (IBHS) was 570 but because it was his second choice, he was not considered for admission. For IBHS, priority was given to all pupils who made the school their first choice. In addition, IBHS did not give scholarship to students from poor families and their school fees were far from what most middle-class parents could afford. When he was told his score and how he missed going to any of the two schools, he was very sad. His headteacher gave him credit for doing so well and explained to him why he was not considered for admission for that year. He encouraged him not to lose hope despite the setback.

On his way back to the village, he was thinking of how his grandmother would feel and what she would say and do. He was crying when he explained to his grandmother all that his headmaster told him. She said, *"Kinni? Irọ nla!*[3] *Irọ nla ni!*[4] We're going together to your school tomorrow to see your *em-masta.* He must make sure you go to that school where they will give you everything free as he once told me or else....?

"Mama, it doesn't work that way," he tried to explain to his grandmother who did not disappoint him with the way she reacted to the bad news.

"Keep quiet. How does it work? When we get there, you will see."

The next day, and very early in the morning, they went to see the headmaster. Once seated in his office, he said, "Mama, good morning."

"My son said you told him he would not be going to that high school that would make him to be a governor of our region in future, is that right?" she asked without returning the headmaster's greetings.

"Mama, I am not the one who said Tayọ won't go to the high school. He did well in his common entrance but...."

"But what? If he did well, what's the 'but" again?"

"This is how it works Mama...."

"I don't want to know how it works. Tell me my son is going to that high school. That's the only thing I want to hear this morning. That's how I will know it works."

"I can't tell you that Mama, I am not the one who owns the school. I can't do anything about their school but I know Tayọ will…."

"Thank you. You know…. Because I am a poor old woman, you don't want my grandson to become a lawyer, a doctor and a governor in future. All of you don't want my son to be very rich and powerful like you. That's what you are all doing. You've all conspired to stop him from going to high school but…. em…. em…. Goodbye *em-masta*," she said as she asked Tayọ to follow her out of the headmaster's office in annoyance.

"Please Mama. Tayọ will still go to high school next year."

"*Isọrait.*[5] If you allow." Grandma left the headmaster unconvinced that he was not the one that failed Tayọ in his exam. Tayọ tried to explain to her when they got back to the village but she was still not persuaded.

"Tayọ, you see, that's why I don't trust these schools. You have been coming first, first, first, first, first or second in all your examinations from primary 1 to primary 6. You always got prizes every year. *Abi beekọ?*[6] Everybody in all our area knows this. *Ọlọgbọn ọmọ ni ọ.*[7] What the *sukul* people said was true for six years, they're now saying it is no longer true. How can I believe them? Now that it's time for you to move forward to *ile-iwe giga*,[8] they denied you. My son, you did not fail. They failed. They are liars. What they're saying is rubbish. I hope they won't do the same thing with Dupẹ."

"God will do it for me next year Mama."

"That is true my son. Those people can't do it for you, I know. They can't. They won't. But our God and my ancestors will do it for you and put all of them to shame."

Tayọ resigned to fate. As time went on, Grandmother was finding it difficult to cope with taking care of Tayọ, Dupẹ and herself since the help she used to get from her husband was no more there. She sent him to his father in Ibadan so he could decide on what he would like him to do next. His father had been offered an appointment as a day-watchman in a construction company and he worked twelve hours day shift Monday to Saturday with a meagre monthly salary. When he got to Ibadan, his father sent him straight to their family house in Igọṣun which was in the heart of the city. It was an old mud house in a cluttered area. It had no electricity supply, tap water, toilet, bathroom or kitchen. The house was traditional to the core. Each of the six tenements had one small window and an entrance door. In fact, there was not much difference between his village house and his family house in the city except that his grandfather's house was large and well maintained. He and other relatives living in the Ibadan house needed to beg some neighbours to allow them to use their bathrooms and toilets. Any day they failed to wake up very early to wash in the open space in front of their house, which they often did to avoid passers-by seeing them, they would postpone doing that or go and beg their neighbours who were fortunate to have toilet and bathroom. It was a tough life in the city for him.

He was asked by his father to come to his place of work from Monday to Saturday. The first day he got there, his father asked him which trade he would like to learn: driving, carpentry, welding, painting or machine operator. He told Tayọ to look at how the young apprentices and their bosses in the company were enjoying their work. His father compared himself to the apprentices' bosses who were his age mate but were better off than he.

He said, "Tayọ, start to learn a trade now that you're still young. If I had known, I would have done the same when I was young. If I did, things would have turned out for me better than this. I was a successful farmer but if I had added trading to that, I would have made use of that knowledge when farming failed me. I'm saying this from experience. Do you hear this clearly?"

Tayọ looked at his father straight in the eyes but said nothing for a few minutes as he was short of words. He was surprised his father offered him those pieces of advice instead of telling him to further his education considering how many times he had told him he wanted him to become a lawyer or a doctor when he was in primary school. Later, he summed up courage and said almost crying, "Sorry Baba, I would rather go to high school than learn any trade. I will not be happy learning any trade. No. No."

"If that's your decision, no problem. But from now, you will start to fend for yourself as I could not finance your high school education with my meagre monthly salary and with many mouths to feed."

In no time, Tayọ became one of the loaders and off-loaders of building materials in that company. He was doing this because he was not guaranteed any other means of livelihood. All of them doing that job were often called derogatory name of *meija-meiload* in their language. Their job was quite different from the one for the apprentices. They loaded lorries with building materials for the building sites where they were needed. They would go with the drivers to offload the materials at different destinations. It was not a job for a lazy person. So, he started as a *meija-meiload* boy. The apprentices were treated well and they were taught how to do their jobs in a professional way. Their bosses rewarded them daily with some money, food and drinks. They would later become lorry drivers, painters, bricklayers or machine operators after their graduation. They looked down and made jest of *meija-meiload* boys. They saw them as unserious and undecided elements because they were not ready to go to school or learn a trade. Tayọ was confused as many people in the company had heard from his father that he had refused to become an apprentice though he had been told he could not go further in his education. To many in the company, he was being arrogant and foolish.

He started following one particular lorry driver. His lorry had no roof at the back. They often loaded bags of cement, pieces of planks, roofing sheets, bags of nails and other building materials into the lorry for onward delivery to other different building sites. The journey at times could be horrible. Their round-tripping might be hundreds of miles most of the time. The wind blowing into the moving lorry was a punishment for those of them who always sat at the back with the building materials when the driver was at full speed. The windy experience was better than when it rained. The driver would ask his senior apprentices to join him in the front seat where they could wind up the window glass for comfort while Tayọ, the other meija meiload boys, and the young apprentices would be soaked in water at the back of the lorry. There was always a big tarpaulin inside the lorry but it was meant to cover the bags of cement or other building materials that rain might spoil. Before rain would start, the driver would park the lorry by the roadside and asked the boys to spread the tarpaulin over all the building materials that could not withstand water and asked them to sit round the edges of it so that wind would not blow it away. The company put more emphasis on their business than on the lives of the boys. On their journeys at times, they often witnessed motor accidents. Once they managed to find their way out of the accident scene which might take hours, the journey would continue. Tayọ and those boys often thought such accidents would happen to them one day as their lorry drivers had had near-misses

many times. But he was between the devil and the deep
blue sea.

Tayọ had an unforgettable work experience when he left the
company his father was working with. His coming to the
city was like jumping out of the frying pan into the fire. He
thought one day to impress it upon his father how terrible
his suffering was. He told him that he would run away from
home and put everybody in trouble as they would be looking
for him everywhere. To his surprise, his father wished him
well wherever he ran to. He thanked him for letting him
know of his intention. Tayọ could not believe what he heard.
His father used to show him some love but how everything
just changed baffled him. He became confusion personified
during that time. Still, he did not want to learn a trade. His
mission was to go further in his education but how and
when, he himself did not know. Going back to the village
was not an option. He was at the crossroads.

*"How could none of my parents show some little mercy? I think
I'm very unlucky. God, please do something to help me if you are
there,"* he was saying to himself one day when he was alone.

One Friday, he went with other boys as usual in the same
lorry on a very long journey to deliver building material to
some building sites. He came back home very late and tired.
He lay down on his sleeping mat and slept off. An hour
later, someone knocked on his room door. He woke up
startled. He went and opened the door without even asking

who it was that had come to disturb his sleep. The person turned out to be one of his distant uncles, Mr Sunday, who was a neighbour.

"Good evening Tayọ," he greeted.

"Good evening sir," he responded though he knew there was nothing good in that evening.

"I've checked on you many times today. When did you come back home?"

"Sorry sir. I came back home just over an hour ago."

"Have you started learning any trade in your father's place of work? I remember you told me one time that you decided not to?"

"Not yet sir. I only join some other boys to load and offload building materials from the company to other building sites scattered all over many towns and cities. Doing that earns me some money to take care of myself," he said emotionally.

"How much are you paid each day or each week for the trips?"

"It depends on what the driver feels like giving me. It is subject to how far the journey is and how stressful the loading and offloading of the building materials are. I learnt we're supposed to be given five naira for each journey but the driver gives me two or three naira per journey at times. I'm not sure how much he gives his apprentices," he explained.

He was not sure why Sunday wanted to know all those pieces of information.

"Does your father give you money to buy food or you spend part of the money you earn to feed yourself?"

"If he has money, he gives me to buy food but I spend part of my money if he doesn't."

Mr Sunday looked him straight in the eyes and shook his head. Tayọ knew he was shocked by his revelation about how he had been coping.

"Okay. Can you work as a household help if there's any opportunity for that somewhere?" Sunday asked. Before Tayọ could respond, he continued, "I have one godly woman who is looking for such a person as soon as possible. You will be living with her family in another area of the city. In addition to taking care of what you will eat and accommodation, you will be paid a small monthly income. Are you happy to do this?"

Tayọ quickly thought about it. He saw it to be an opportunity to run away from home where he was not sure maybe he belonged or not. Also, what he was doing for a living and its attendant daily risks and insults from everybody, who could not understand that he was neither arrogant nor lazy, made him decide to accept the offer at once.

"Where exactly is the place sir?"

"She lives in Agodi Gate, just some miles off the university campus. She sells women's goods in one of the girls' hostels on the university campus where I work as a security officer. Her husband's driver takes her to and from work every day except on Sundays. She opens her shop at 2 pm and closes at 9 pm. The woman is very nice and well-known on campus. She approached me few weeks ago to ask if I could get her a young person - male or female - who is hard-working and honest. I had asked my first son if he could go there and work but he said 'No'. He is not ready to live away from home for now," the man took his time to explain as much as he knew about the woman.

Without any further thought, Tayọ said, "I will do it sir. I can even start tomorrow but will it be possible for me to leave the place when I want to start secondary school?" Though he was not sure who would send him to pursue his education dream, he was optimistic that he would go to high school one day.

"I think that won't be a problem at all. The woman, Mrs Aka, is not highly educated but she loves education so much. In fact, two of her children are studying in our university. I think they will allow you to go to high school whenever you are ready. They can even help you to get admission into a high school or possibly sponsor you if you prove yourself as a responsible, honest and hardworking boy." Thus, he was told so much about the goodness of Mrs Ruth Aka.

"Thank you very much sir. I'll make sure I work hard and I'll be honest," he promised his uncle.

"You are welcome. I will go and inform your father about this new development as soon as possible so he won't be worried about your whereabouts."

Sunday was very happy about his decision. Between two evils, Tayọ chose the one which he thought was better. At home with his father, he was no longer sure of what he could do towards his education dream. He thought if he could go to a new environment to experience a new life, there may be a different way of moving forward academically.

"Sir, I'm ready to go with you to that place and start the work tomorrow. Thank you, sir."

Tried as he did, he could not sleep well during the night because of the sudden new development. He thought he was dreaming and felt afraid that the man could come back and say it was not true.

He lay on his mat and cast his mind back to his primary school days. He brought to his remembrance one story in one of their Yorùbá textbooks about the inhuman treatment often given to house helps and slaves. Pupils were made to believe then that only those who were not serious with their education and those who were lazy would end up as house helps or slaves.

He always remembered one very popular song in the textbook which teaches hard work:

"Bata rẹ a ro ko ka

Bata rẹ́ á ro ko ko ka

Tí o bá kawe rẹ

Bata rẹ a ro ko ko ka.

Bata rẹ a wọ pẹrẹṣẹ nilẹ

Bata rẹ a wọ pẹrẹṣẹ nilẹ

Ti o ba a kawe rẹ

Bata rẹ a wọ pẹrẹṣẹ nile.

Tayọ kawe rẹ

Bata rẹ a ro ko ko kà

Peter kawe rẹ

Bata rẹ a ro ko ko ka

Bukọla kawe rẹ

Bata rẹ a ro ko ko ka.[9]

Everybody's prayer then was never to become either a house help or a slave. In Tayọ's case, he was neither lazy nor unserious about his education but he had found himself in a situation he could not help. In the following few hours, he would become what he never thought of - a house help even though he had performed brilliantly in primary school. Failing to get that scholarship to study at GCI still hurt him. But even if he had been given admission to IBHS which was an option then, he knew his father would not have been able to afford the fees. He blamed his parents who were alive, hale and hearty but had consigned him to that personal decision-making point in his life. He remembered one quotation he had come across that says, 'Real misfortune is not just a matter of being hungry and thirsty, it is a matter of knowing that there are people who want you to be hungry and thirsty.' The writer, from Tayọ's point of view, must have had his own parents in mind when he wrote that. He thought if the two of them had not gone their separate ways, life probably would have turned out differently for their children.

The following day, he did not go to his father's place of work. In the afternoon, Sunday and Tayọ left for the university campus to meet Mrs Ruth Aka. When they got there, he was handed over to her. Thereafter, a short conversation between Sunday and Mrs Aka took place. His haggard-looking appearance was the first thing the woman noticed. His long and hollow neck, thin legs and sunken eyes could not be hidden from any prying eyes. But any other worried, confused and neglected boy like him could not have looked any different. When he noticed the way

Mrs Aka was looking at him, his prayer at that point in time was that she should not reject him straight off.

"Mr Sunday, do you think this boy is healthy enough to do this type of job? It's a very strenuous job as you know coupled with the fact that he will still do more work at home."

"Yes, he is. I have always known him to be healthy and very hardworking. I don't think he's ever had any serious illness. Madam, try and see if he could work with you, don't mind his appearance. I can vouch for him."

Tayọ overheard the two of them discussing his suitability for the job. After few minutes of further discussion, she thanked Sunday for finding her a house help at last. Tayọ heaved a sigh of relief.

When she closed for that day and they were on their way home in the family car, Tayọ was thinking of many things and asking himself many questions:

"How would the new environment look like? Have I been sold to this woman without my knowledge? Will they be hostile to me like people at home? What will be the nature of my work? How long will I be here for? How much would I be paid every month? Will there be any freedom for me to play at all? When will I be sleeping and waking up? Will I be allowed to go to secondary school in due course?" Those were questions with no immediate answers.

Mrs Ruth Aka and her driver were chatting on many topics of interest on their way back home that night. Tayọ kept quiet because those questions he failed to ask himself before his uncle brought him down were haunting him. He tried to see if he could identify their routes right from the university but that was not possible because it was night time.

That day, he started work as a house boy. Unlike his family house, his employer's house was a modern storey building with all the amenities. Mrs Aka and her family occupied the upper flat while another family tenanted the lower flat but her family was not the owner of the building. She introduced him to her husband and their children that were at home. Before they had supper, he was shown the kitchen, the bathroom and the living room where he would be sleeping after everyone would have retired to their bedrooms. He was given a mattress on which he would be sleeping. There was a small bench on the way to the living room from the kitchen where he was told he would be eating his food. He was given his own plates and spoons to be kept separately from others. He was told to always wash his hands after he had finished doing anything. He was not to eat his food until others had been served and had started eating. He was instructed to always bless his food before eating and to pray to God to continue to provide for the family and those that did not have something to eat. He was told to clean the apartment rooms every morning and to dust the tv, the tv stand, stereo sound system, drawers, tables, chairs, photo frames and so many other things in the flat. He was

warned never to make use of any of them without
permission.

"If anyone of these items is damaged," Mrs Aka warned him,
"you will pay for it. Your monthly income is seventeen naira
which isn't enough to buy any of these items. Since you will
be fed and housed freely, that amount is still a lot of money
though."

"Thank you, ma. I will be careful with all of them ma."

At the start, it was incredibly isolating for Tayọ: not eating
with the family, not watching television with them,
separate place to sit and eat, separate cutlery, plate and cup
to use, things to touch and not to touch, when to talk and
when to act as a deaf and dumb, sleeping only after
everyone had gone to sleep no matter how late it was, all
house cleaning reserved for him, etc. Despite all the dos and
don'ts given to him by his new boss, he accepted the new
challenge as a good trouble to experiment with. He was
happy he would be living in a beautiful environment for a
change, eating good quality food and earning some money
at the end of every month. Those things gave him some
comfort. On the university campus where they traded, he
was the odd one around. People could easily identify who
he was without any introduction whenever they came to
their shop because, appearance, as they say, shows the
manner.

"Mama, is this your new house help? How are you young
boy? What's your name? Are you from Ibadan?" Tayọ could

not remember how many countless times customers asked
him and Mrs Aka those questions.

His coping mechanism whenever he was down and feeling
lonely was that, one day, he would pass his school entrance
exam, leave for high school, study hard and become
somebody important later in life.

One of his major duties was emptying the waste bins in
their flat every three days. As the house boy, he had the
singular honour of taking the filled-up refuse bags to the
dumping site. That job was usually done about 6 am. The
dumping site was about half a kilometre to their house. The
road was always busy around that time with vehicles and
people. He would carry the heavy black waste bag on his
head as he walked the distance. On his way back home from
the location, he would see his age mates in neat uniforms on
their way to school. They would be at every bus stop
waiting for their school buses. The luxurious buses were
given to each high school by the then military government
out of the largesse of petroleum oil boom in Nigeria in the
early 70s. The buses were a beauty to behold. Students in
the buses would be chatting or singing to show how joyful
they were as their drivers honked the horns for other road
users to give way for them to pass. Students must not be late
to school but there were no bus lanes. The drivers needed to
beg other road users or force their ways out from traffic
jams which was a regular occurrence. Tayọ always stayed
some poles away from one particular bus stop to watch the
lucky students enjoying their lives. They would be on the

line according to which school they attended. When a bus arrived, the students for that particular school would climb into the bus one by one.

"God, why have you given these students special privileges? Are they all more brilliant than I? Why are they looking so radiant and well fed? Why am I from my poor family? God, are you partial in your creation?"

Before he would finish his endless questions, tears would run down his cheeks. At that moment, insecurity, hatred and disappointment often took over his life. He thought of taking his own life to escape what he was going through. But Mrs Ruth Aka often told him that with patience and hard work, there was no setback that human beings could not overcome. Though he believed her, it was tough to be on the receiving end of the stick. His wish when he was young was to read many books, get as much knowledge as possible from those books because he wanted to become a medical doctor or a lawyer, which was once his father's dream for him. He had heard that becoming a doctor or a lawyer was not for lazy readers. Starry-eyed, Tayọ dreamed dreams. But he realised that dream and reality are poles apart. In real life, you get to the crossroads and later find your way, but at times you hit a dead end. In dreams, you might see yourself as a successful businessman, sport man, actor, musician, Nobel laureate, Pope or the president of the USA swimming in wealth until you wake up and feel sorry for yourself.

CHAPTER SIX

verything happens for a reason - Aristotle

E Mrs Ruth Aka was not a native of Ibadan but she had been living there for such a long time that she knew many areas of the vast city. She was married to a retired senior air force officer. She was called 'Mummy' by everybody and so, Tayọ adopted that tag for her. Her family was living a comfortable life in the city. She was a Christian by conversion and she was God-fearing. After a week in his new place of work and after careful observation, Mrs Aka called Tayọ into the living room one day and asked him many probing questions about his background: where he was coming from; how he got to her place; his education and what he wanted to become in life.

"You are called 'Tayọ', what are your other names?"

"My baptismal name is Samuel, my father's name is Kọlapọ," he said shyly.

"So, you are a Christian by birth?"

"Yes, ma."

"Which church do you attend on Sundays?"

"Saint Peter's Anglican Church, ma."

"Where's that located?"

"It's in Aremọ, near Ode-Aje on your way to Agugu Ọrẹmeji-Idi-Obi area by bus ma."

"Sorry, I don't know much of that area."

"Are both your parents still living?"

"Yes, ma."

"Were you living with them before now?"

"No, ma."

"How many wives does your father have because I know Ibadan men love women too much?" she asked jocularly.

"Four wives."

"I know (she laughs). I trust them. Are all the wives still living with your father?" she pressed further.

"I think three are still married to him, my mother left him when I was a baby," he said emotionally.

"You have been living where and with whom then?"

"At my mother's village with my grandmother," he covered his face with his hands as he was feeling uneasy with the questions.

"Don't feel bad Tayọ that I'm asking you these questions. I only want to know who you are and what I can learn from your life story. Is that ok with you?"

"Yes, Mummy."

"How old are you?"

"I am fifteen, ma."

"My last born is just a year older than you. He is now in a boarding secondary school. He is tall and handsome," she told him with pride. He looked at himself again and felt sorry for his poor appearance. When she stopped talking, Tayọ made to go but she called him back and said, "Tayọ, remind me tomorrow to give you some of my son's used clothes."

"Thank you, ma, I will." He was happy to hear that. He left for the kitchen to do some cleaning. He noticed that she was a good woman as his uncle had told him. He knew later that she was the only wife of her husband and that she had four children, two boys and two girls. The first born, Dele, was then studying medicine at the University of Ibadan, her second child, a girl, was also studying at the same university. The other girl and Kola, the last born, were in boarding schools outside Ibadan city. Both the man and his wife were natives of Ikalẹ.

During the holidays, all their children came back home. When he saw how they were pampered, he was sad that he was born into a devil-may-care family. They ate a balanced diet. It was there he really understood what 'balanced diet' was. They didn't eat just anything for breakfast, lunch or dinner. There was a timetable for what food to eat, soft drink to take with a particular menu and what type of ice cream or tea to follow. It was there he also knew what 'brunch' meant. Their parents bought them new clothes and shoes depending on their academic performances. One time when their father was presenting them the new presents, he assured those still in the high school that he was ready to sponsor them to any university in the world once they could do well in their studies. They were very happy and grateful to their parents for their motivation. Tayọ was flabbergasted seeing what was happening. He had never witnessed such a joyous family occasion. Kọla, their last born, called him to help him take his own presents to his room. On the way, he nearly wept.

He thought, *"If I have had this type of opportunity from a loving family, I don't think I would be here working as a houseboy. Some were born lucky. I will work hard and see what happens in the future. I think I will make it too."*

Throughout their holiday, their daily routine was sleep, shower, eat, do some holiday home work, watch videos, read their dad's newspapers, entertain friends and exercise.

Kọla loved Tayọ as if he were his blood brother. Immediately he came for holiday, he gave Tayọ many of his used clothes and shoes to complement what his mother had given him before he came back home. Tayọ began to see a change in his wellbeing. He ate good food and dressed well though his daily work schedule was taxing. Whenever he was accused of not doing something properly, Kọlá would go to him and ask him to take it lightly.

He would tell him, "Tayọ, it's one of those things. You'll live to tell the story." At times he would shout at everybody, "Leave this boy alone pleaaaase."

He would ask him to go with them to night parties but he was hardly given any chance to attend as he was often told that going to parties was not one of the reasons he was employed. He agreed with that but it saddened him a lot.

One Sunday morning, Kola told him that in the evening he would like both of them to go to the cinema. He told him not to tell anybody or he would not be allowed to go with him. Both of them planned how they would execute their plan. Tayọ asked him where they would get the gate fee, but he was told not to worry. He was ecstatic because that was the first time he would be going to the cinema to watch a film. Previously, Kola had told him about many films as he was a regular attendee in company with his friends. They all went to church that Sunday as usual. When they came back from church, they ate their lunch and he quickly washed all the plates and did all other things he needed to do as Ḳọla had told him to do. Towards evening, Ḳọla told his mother that he would like Tayọ to accompany him to a friend's house. She gave them the go ahead but warned both of them not to come back late as Tayo's work would have piled up by night time.

Both got to Scala Cinema at 8:50 pm having stayed longer at Ḳọla's friend's house. Ḳọlá bought the two of them some suya[1] which they relished with two bottles of Coca Cola. In Ibadan City in the 70s and 80s, going to the cinema for the young and the old was one of the best ways to catch fun especially during the weekend. Popular cinemas then were the Queen's Cinema at Adamasingba, KS Cinema at Orita Mefa, Rex Cinema, Odeon Cinema at Oke-Ado and Scala Cinema in Ṣabo which was mostly populated by the Hausa. They all offered a variety of films ranging from Western to Yorùbá, Chinese and Indian. For the best Indian films, Scala was the preferred cinema to go. That night, the Indian film being shown was *Dostana*, a 1980 action-drama film which starred Amitabh Bachchan, Shatrughan Sinha, Zeenat Aman, Amrish Puri and others. The film started at 9:55 pm. Ḳọla and Tayọ sat on one of the middle rows. Lights were switched off. Tayọ was afraid but Ḳọlá eased his fear. The film started with a trailer. The fierce-looking lead actor in the film was holding a big automatic gun pointed straight at the audience. Tayọ shut his eyes tightly thinking the actor was about to shoot all of them dead. He stood up, ready to take to his heels but Kọla held him down and told him not to behave like a village boy. He explained what was happening on the screen to him and told him that nothing dangerous would happen to anyone in the cinema room even if all the actors and actresses were shot dead. He believed him, sat down with some confidence and watched the rest of the film with interest.

When the film ended at 12 am, they left the cinema but the two of them became afraid of what fate awaited them at home. They knew everybody would have been looking for them wondering their whereabouts. They might have gone to the police station to report them missing. They had no plausible excuse to explain their absence from home for such long hours without telling anyone where they were going. Tayọ was sure he would be sent packing that day unfailingly. After wasting more time thinking of what their excuse would be, they finally got back home and met everybody outside including some other relatives and neighbours. Kola and Tayo were led to the living room and a barrage of questions were fired at them by everybody at the same time, especially at Kọla who they pointed finger at as the culprit, teaching Tayọ nonsense. The commotion they caused that night was an unusual occurrence in the family. Kọla first lied that they were arrested by police because they fought with some boys on their way. After much pressure to tell the truth, they revealed everything. They were asked to lie down to receive some strokes of cane but Mrs Aka and

others begged Ḳọla's dad on their behalf not to cane them.
He accepted their pleas but warned the two of them never
to try that again. He rebuked Ḳọla sternly. He told him Tayọ
would not have thought of doing something like that if he
had not encouraged him. From that day, he was asked never
to send Tayọ on any errand or ask him to go out with him
to anywhere.

"Tayọ, sorry if I have caused you some trouble by asking
you to go with me to the cinema. I did it because I believe
you should be given some time to enjoy yourself though I
knew it wouldn't go fine with the family. We've done it but
I'm happy you're left out of the blame though you might
have thought otherwise," Ḳọla told Tayọ few days after the
incident.

"You know I was reluctant to go with you but thank God I
wasn't sent back home. I was expecting harsher punishment
for what we did but we both escaped that. Next time, we
won't do that again." Tayọ said.

"We might if they still don't give you some free time to go
out with me even if it's just once in a blue moon."

"Ḳọla, I won't unless Mummy specifically gives me
permission to go out with you. Remember I once told you I
promised my uncle who introduced me to Mummy that I
would be obedient and hardworking. I won't like to let him
down."

"Well, that's okay for now."

After that incident, Tayọ carried out his duties with total devotion. Diligently, he continued his tooth-and-claw life struggle.

In his third month as a houseboy, he again sat the common entrance examination into secondary school. Prior to that time, he had been praying to God to help him in life. The military government in power in Nigeria at that time decided at last to hand over power to a democratic government. Many political parties were registered to contest the scheduled elections. One of the parties, the United Nigeria Party (UNP) promised free and compulsory education from primary to tertiary level as one of its cardinal programmes. Mrs Aka's family were not against Tayọ furthering his education. Her first son, Dele, who was a medical student, took interest in him and his future academic pursuit. He told their mum that he would be helping Tayọ to prepare for his exam so that he would pass well. She was happy to hear that and encouraged him to do so. Any little time when he was not busy, he would solve some past questions given to him by Dele. Once he submitted his work to Dele, he would mark it immediately and ask him to come for some explanation on those questions he got wrong. It went on and on like that for three months. Any time Tayọ did very well in any given past questions, Dele would show everyone in the family his work and tell them that Tayọ was a very brilliant boy. At times, he would give him some sweet or biscuit or a bottle of Coca Cola just to motivate him. Gradually Tayọ's belief that many human beings were wicked was being re-examined. His own parents who were supposed to be his comforters turned out to be his soul troublers whereas people who were not his relatives were giving him hope for the future. He called on God to help him to be like those school students he often met on his way to the refuse dumping site. He also prayed he should be like his boss's children. Every day, he expected his common entrance exam result with high hope.

"Will I get a very high score and beat the cut-off mark this time? What happens if I don't? I pray that must not happen again. These days, I'm always fretful, why God? The examination body need to release this result quickly or else the continued suspense will kill me," Tayọ thought to himself when he was about to sleep one night.

Mrs Aka travelled to Lagos to buy some wares for her shop one day. She came back very late contrary to what she told her family when she was going. Tayọ and her children had thought she would not arrive that day because it was raining heavily. Suddenly, they heard a car being parked outside. Tayọ quickly ran down the stairs to see who it was. It turned out to be Mrs Aka. Others joined him to welcome her. They brought out all the merchandise she bought from the vehicle. Tayọ joyfully carried one heavy basket of goods on his head as he was climbing the stairs leading into their flat. He was on the middle of the stairs when his legs slipped. He and all that he carried fell and rolled down the stairs. He got wounded and many breakable items in the bag got smashed. That night, he nearly ran away. He was called into the living room and called names. "This is sad Tayọ. You just spoilt my day completely. I left this house very early today and came back this late. It rained for the whole day but I managed to buy my wares. I didn't have any time to eat. But see what you've made of all my effort. This saddens me a lot."

"Sorry Mummy. I didn't mean to…."

"Keep quiet and let me talk or I'll…. How dare you do this to me? This is very sad. Just put yourself in my position, will you be happy tonight?" Mrs Aka asked. As he kept quiet and looked from one person to another, he was called names even though it was the first serious mistake he had made since he had been working with them. He looked at all the broken items on the floor with sadness. He wanted to beg and talk, but he kept quiet as he did not want to infuriate Mrs Aka any further. Kọla, his friend and defender on many occasions, was also helpless.

"I must run away from this place tomorrow. Oh my God, this is terrible. I know what happened was very bad. This shouldn't have happened. No. Why God? I injured myself, nobody cares about that, everyone is more concerned about the broken items. I can understand but…. I feel sorry for her loss but…. Why did I slip and cause all this trouble? I've spoilt the day for everybody. This is a sad night for me. Where will I run to? Apart from this, I will disappoint myself and Uncle Sunday who introduced me to the family," he thought to himself.

After the dressing down, he left the living room for his own bench outside the kitchen, his night terribly spoiled. He was denied his dinner. It was then he started sobbing silently. If he had a choice, he would have left that evening but he was on the horns of a dilemma.

The following morning once he woke up, Tayọ knocked at Mrs Aka's door. She knew he was the one. "Good morning, Mummy. I'm really sorry for all I did last night," he prostrated himself and begged her for forgiveness.

"That's okay Tayọ, all of us make mistakes. I'm getting over it. Yesterday was just a day to forget as I said last night. But don't let that mistake repeat itself. I know you injured yourself. Hope the pain isn't much. You'll need to take some paracetamol after your breakfast and put some Vaseline to the affected area. Just be more careful about how you do your things all the time. Is that clear?"

"Yes ma. Very clear ma. I will be very careful next time ma. Thank you, ma."

Leaving that behind him, he continued with his work. He was in his seventh month when Uncle Sunday came to see him at their shop. He came with one envelope in his hand which Tayọ did not notice. His uncle exchanged greetings with Mrs Aka. After that, he called Tayọ aside and gave him the envelope. He showed it to Mrs Aka and she asked him to open it. It turned out to be his result slip and an admission letter into Origbo High School, Ibadan. He shouted, jumped on his uncle and humbly thanked Mrs Aka for everything. Mrs Aka hugged, congratulated him on his success and said,

"Clever you Tayọ. Well done. Let me see the result."

She looked at the result slip and the admission letter and proudly showed both to her customers who were in the shop. All of them rejoiced with him. For the first time on that campus, he felt elated to see people appreciating him. When customers had left the shop, Mrs Aka carefully read the admission letter and noticed that he would start his high school the following September. She called Sunday and had a long discussion with him all based on how he could help her get another house help once Tayọ went to school. His uncle promised to try his best again. Throughout that day on the campus, his mind was not on what they were doing in the shop but on his new status as a would-be secondary school student like Kọla.

"I will be inside one of those glistening school buses one day. I will sing with other students and dress like them. I will be able to speak English very fluently and I will cease to be called a houseboy. When I finish my high school, I shall come to this university to study medicine. God, I thank you. Mummy, I thank you. Uncle Dele, I thank you. I thank everyone, I thank you all." Those were the feelings that occupied his mind throughout that day.

When they got back home that night, it was joy unlimited for the family.

Dele said, "I told all of you that he would pass his common entrance exam with flying colours. I have been proved right. Tayọ is so intelligent. Believe me."

"I knew that too," Kọla said. Everyone congratulated him. He was given special dinner which he ate together with others in the dining room for the first time. He could not believe how a person's life could be turned around within a twinkling of an eye. Right from the moment he collected that wonderful result slip and admission letter, things took a positive turn for him. On campus where they were trading, everyone was calling him a student though he had yet to start in his high school. Mrs Aka asked her children to teach him lessons on the subjects he would be taught in school. Any time a visitor came, he was introduced to them as a high school-student-to-be. She would ask her visitors to help get her another house help to replace him. It was like a dream how his exam success had brought him respect and love. The most exciting thing was that he was allowed to sit in the living room to watch television and eat with other members of the family. He was promoted from his bench, which served as his dining, to the family dining circle. It was like a magic because he could not believe what was happening.

One weekend when they were all relaxing in the living room, Kọla asked,

"Now that Tayọ has done well in his exam and getting ready to go and move on, would he be allowed to go with us to parties, football matches, cinema and other places especially on Saturdays? I am asking these questions because all the experiences he'll have from such outings will help him do well in school."

"You have a point there, I think," Dele said before Mrs Aka could say a word.

"Both of you are right. But who would be doing his work for him on Saturdays?" she asked.

"Mum, that's no problem. I could help him with some tasks and he could do more on Fridays after both of you have come back from the campus. What about that?"

"I am not promising anything for now but we will see how that will work out."

CHAPTER SEVEN

I*t's not who you are that holds you back, it's who you think you're not - Hanock McCarty*

The general elections were conducted. The United Nigeria Party (UNP) did not win the presidential election but won in all the states in the western region where their national leader came from. The western states where the party won were Lagos, Ogun, Ọyọ, Bendel and Ondo popularly called LOOBO states. UNP alleged that the elections were flawed with rigging and other atrocities all over the country but their leader promised that their party's cardinal programmes would start once they were sworn in.

In his political broadcast after the election, he said, "I congratulate all of you today on voting massively for our party in the states where we have won though we know some more states we would have won were rigged by the

enemies of the people. Thank you for your support. Thank
you for believing in us. Once we are sworn in, we will fight
corruption with everything we've got everywhere we see it.
We're in this horrible situation today in this country
because of corruption at every level of governance. It is
something that we talk about but hardly do anything about.
Little by little, it has become a cankerworm that has eaten
deep into every fabric of our society. We have to kill it
before it kills all of us. With this incoming government in
our states, our view on corruption must change. Bearing
this in mind, we will do everything possible as leaders to
make you buy into us. We will lead by example. Scrutinize
and tell us any time we fail to do what we promised we
would do. We will earn our leadership every day. In the
mid-1960s, the late Labour Prime Minister in Britain,
Harold Wilson once said, 'A week is a long time in politics.'
By that standard, I think, our country has wasted more than
enough time doing nothing to be great. We must change
this horrible narrative.

"From now, the down-and-outs of our states will begin to
enjoy the benefits of supporting a progressive party. To
start with, we're going to declare our assets, so you all know
what each of us has and at the end of every political office,
we will declare our assets to know what we are going out
with. Transparency will be our watchword. Also, and as we
have promised, education that has been commodified for
ages will be made free in our states. All schools from

primary to high school would be supplied with free books,
stationery and all teaching facilities. School fees are hereby
abolished as we promised during our electioneering. It
would become a criminal offence for any parent to refuse to
send his/her children to school. Any school or parent that
fails to adhere strictly to these rules will be dealt with
legally. Our government will be a stickler for the rule of law.
We will respect the court of law as arbiters between the
government and the governed. Our elected governors, local
government leaders and councillors are all here to serve
you. From now on, we're your servants. We are in
government to educate our children who are the leaders of
tomorrow. We are here to bridge the gap between the haves
and the have-nots. This is a new era. This is a new dawn.
We need your cooperation, our wonderful citizens, more
than ever before. We should all start thinking about the
nitty gritty of the future greatness of our dear country.
We're starting from here. Together, we can do it. Together,
we shall do it. Together we shall succeed. We will all enjoy
the benefits of democracy and good governance which have
eluded us for a long time. Ours will be a model of how
government should be run. Generations yet unborn will
read about the legacy we will leave behind, and, our
achievements will surely outlive us. Thank you all and God
bless."

That political broadcast from the presidential candidate and
leader of the UNP, Chief Ọbaniyi Awoniyi was the best

broadcast any Nigerian political leader had ever made. Tayọ
knew for sure from the broadcast that finance would not be
a hindrance again in his pursuit of education. He prayed for
the success of Chief Awoniyi, his lieutenants and the party
every day as he knew they were godsent.

"When are you leaving us finally?" Mrs Aka asked Tayọ one
Sunday during lunch.

"I will leave when the new school session starts ma. Maybe
a week to the school resumption, but I am not sure yet," he
said happily.

"Will you be coming to say hello to us during the
weekends?" Kọla chipped in.

"I will be doing that not only on weekends but also during
holidays."

Tayọ was asked to go and inform his father. He went and
told him. His father was remorseful and welcoming. He
congratulated him on his success and promised to render
any help within his power to support him. "It's good to
believe in what you want to do and work very hard towards
it. No matter how difficult it is, you will achieve it. This is
what I have seen in what is happening in your life," his
father said.

"Thank you, Daddy. I'm happy to hear this."

"That's it. It's God that has done it for you at His own time.
Thank Him."

"Thank You God," Tayọ said.

"Now, hear this my son. My aim before life's misfortune befell me was to send all my male children to school, even up to university. But that dream changed when I was finding it very difficult to take care of myself not to mention of taking care of my children. My farm business collapsed and I didn't have money again. You have seen how hard this life could be when you lose everything. When you start high school, face your studies, never join bad gangs which can corrupt your manners. Always remember the son of whom you are. I am poor and I don't want any problem from anywhere to add to my problem. Tell Mrs Aka when you get back that I will come and thank her and her family for the help they have rendered to you."

Listening to that from his father was like listening to a beautiful music. He had changed from being a tough-talking father to a loving one who could advise and encourage his son.

Mrs Aka and Tayọ arrived home one night from their shop. Immediately they got home, they ate dinner. He was too tired to do any other taxing work. So, he packed all the plates into the sink hoping to wash them first thing the next morning since he had been allowed such luxury. He left the kitchen for the living room and fell asleep. During that sleep, he dreamed that a man was coming towards him. The more Tayọ ran, the closer the man was getting to him but he ran and ran until there was no more power in him. He collapsed. The man got to where Tayọ lay as he was screaming his head off. His bodily structure was abnormal; everything about him was over-sized. He had big teeth, arms, eyes, feet, ears, mouth and nose. He also had a scaly skin and a long belly button. He looks like an ogre. Some voices were saying something gibberish to the man which made his steps rhythmical as he went round and round Tayọ. Tayọ wanted to stand up and run but there was no strength in him. He continued to shout but his voice did not come out.

At a point and with a very loud voice the man commanded, "Bring that big pot with boiling water for me now." When Tayọ heard that, he tried to stretch his hands forward to beg the man not to do him any harm but he could not move.

The horrible creature stamped his feet on the ground, laughed hysterically and said, "Yes, Tayọ, or whatever they call you, you're dying a horrible death today at last. I was sent on a mission and I must finish you off with this boiling water in my hands in just a minute. Yes…. Yes…. Yes." He was so happy for his about-to-be-accomplished mission.

He raised the hot water pot up carefully and dramatically but before he could do the damage, Tayọ shouted with the last power left in him and opened his eyes. He looked at himself, he was sweating. Inside him, he felt as if a fire was consuming him.

He shouted, "No. No. No. This is real. I'm dead! Mummy, everybody, please come and help me. I'm burning inside. I'm dying. Everybody please, help me." Within minutes, Mrs Aka's family rushed out from their rooms with fright to see him writhing in pain. Initially, they did not move near him but later when he was gasping and struggling to talk, Mr Aka summoned up courage and moved near him. His wife and the children were confused and did not know what to do. Mr Aka felt his body all over and noticed it was very hot.

"Tayọ, no, Tayọ please…. em….em….What happened?" Mrs Aka was shouting.

Dele thought on what to do next. He took their family car key, ran down the stairs and moved their car out from the garage. He ran back upstairs and said, "Let's quickly rush this boy to the hospital."

They all agreed and carried him down into the car almost dying. Dele drove to the main road at full speed while others were fanning and calling Tayọ's name repeatedly.

Tayọ was saying intermittently, "Hot…. water…. heads…. body….big….uh….uh….uh….heads….I'm….dying." His utterances were unintelligible.

At the last turning to the hospital, there was a stationary car right on the middle of the road. Before Dele knew what was happening, he was just few meters from it. Quickly he swerved the car, crossed the culvert, and drove straight into a light pole. As that commotion was unravelling, everyone was shouting, "Jesus, save. God, help. God, help. J-E-E-S-U-S."

Miraculously, the low culvert had reduced the speed of their car and when it hit the pole, much damage was not done. All of them could have perished if not for the culvert. When others were shouting and calling on God and Jesus to help, Tayọ was only saying, "fire…. man….hot….pot….water…." Dele in his confused state of mind said to himself, "This is really a devil's work. God, you must help us and this poor boy."

"Tayọ is dying, please what are we going to do next?" Mrs Aka asked.

Barely five minutes afterwards, they heard the sound of an on-coming vehicle. Mrs Aka and her children who were already crying for help motioned the driver for assistance. The driver, thinking they might be armed robbers, drove past but stopped some few metres from where they were standing. They ran to him and when they explained the situation they were in, the man asked them to bring Tayọ into his car while some of them were told to walk along. Immediately they got to the hospital, the doctor examined him, gave him an injection and administered intravenous fluids for rehydration. He slept off like a log. The doctor informed Mrs Aka and family that there was no cause for alarm though he said he could not diagnose his strange illness until further examination was carried out. She and her children were relieved. The doctor advised them to go back home if that was safe considering the security situation in the city at that time. He asked them to come back later in the day for further briefing. At exactly 1pm in the afternoon, Tayọ woke up a little relaxed. The doctor was by his side when he woke up.

"Please where am I?" Tayọ asked.

"You are in our hospital, young man. How are you feeling?" he asked smiling.

"Are you the tall man with the hot water sir?" Tayọ asked the doctor as he covered his eyes with both hands.

"No. How about the man?"

"I can't say, but I'm scared. Okay, where are Mummy, uncle Dele, Daddy and Kọla?"

"Do you want to see them?"

"Yes." The doctor left the room and invited Mrs Aka in.

"Mummy, please, what happened to me? Did you see that wicked man with a pot brimming with hot water?"

"Sorry Tayọ, I cannot say. And I did not see any man. Don't worry, you'll get over this," she assured him.

"Mummy, but what about those many heads behind the man urging him to kill me? I saw bodiless heads. I'm sure."

"Don't think of them for now Tayọ. At least you can see me and other people are here with you. Will you like to eat some food Tayọ?" Mrs Aka asked Tayọ to change the topic."

"I cannot eat Mummy. Sorry. My body is still hot and I'm in pain. That man wanted to throw hot water at me. Many others were telling him to kill me off. He was happy to kill me. Why were they after my life? What wrong did I do to them? If I had not opened my eyes, what could have…." he started crying.

On his second day in the hospital, he understood that he was rushed down there in the dead of night. After a week there, he was discharged. Mrs Aka was there when he was cleared to go home. She paid the hospital bill and thanked the doctor for everything he did. When they got back home, he narrated all that happened between the strange man and himself up to the time he woke up from that nasty dream and started to shout for help. Thinking such an incident might still occur, he hardly slept deep anymore.

"Tayọ, who have you offended?" Mrs Aka asked him one day after he had recovered fully.

"Nobody ma. I don't know ma."

"Have you watched some horror films lately, maybe here or somewhere else?" Deọla, Mrs Aka's daughter asked.

"I have not watched any horror film," he said tearfully. "May I go and inform my father about this? Maybe he will know, maybe he could help me out."

"That will have to be postponed. I met the pastor of our church yesterday and after I explained what happened to you, he said I should bring you down for prayer. So, tomorrow before we leave for the shop, we will go and see him. Moreover, I've informed your uncle on our campus about what happened but I told him you're being taking good care of."

"It is all right ma," he responded because he believed in the power of prayer.

Early the following day, he started to do some skeletal home activities. During the morning devotion, he did not drowse off as before. He said "Amen" thrice to each prayer point raised. After the prayers, he swept the rooms, dusted the chairs, rearranged the sitting room, cleaned the toilet and bathroom and washed all the dirty plates.

"Mummy, I've finished every other thing, can I go and empty the refuse bin?"

"Yesterday, somebody needed to be called to empty it. He did that and got paid.

"No, mummy. Thank you, ma. You're always so caring.

Actually, Tayọ had missed his normal routine of seeing high school students in their various school buses, singing, drumming and chatting away as if they did not have any care in the world. Knowing he would be starting school that year, he wanted to learn more things from them. He had tried to interact with one of the students one day, but his

inferiority complex prevented him. He moved to talk to him
but recoiled at the last minute. One morning before he got
his admission letter, he was on his way to dump the rubbish.
He saw a schoolboy of his age coming behind him, no one
was close to both of them. He decided to talk to the boy
despite the bin bag on his head. Before the boy walked past
him, he waited and looked himself over. He had on his dirty
clothes which he wore due to the morning housework he
did. In contrast, the boy wore a white shirt, black shorts,
white pair of socks, black school sandals, a brown cap and
carried a brown bag in his hand. He looked very smart. As
the boy walked very quickly past Tayọ as if to avoid him,
Tayọ summoned up courage, moved faster and said to the
boy in his mother tongue, *Kaaarọ.*[1] The boy ignored him,
pretending that he did not hear Tayo's greeting.

"Duro. A bi o gbọ ni?"[2] he said in his native language again. He
wanted to change his communication with the boy into
English but he remembered that people often laughed at
him if he dared to commit grammatical blunder whenever
he tried to speak English. At that point, he stuck to Yorùbá
so that the boy would not make jest of him. As he persisted
to make the boy talk back, he tried to touch him for his
attention.

"Are you mad?" the boy asked, stopped and fired more
questions at Tayọ, "Who are you talking to in vernacular?
Do you think I don't hear what you say? Are you all right? I
wish my teacher is here to punish you for speaking in

Yoruba. Idiot. Go straight and throw away the rubbish you're carrying on your head. Common slave."

Tayọ stood like a statue. He was amazed at the ease with which the boy spoke English and was hurt by the boy's arrogance.

"*Ori iwọ ọmọ yi ti daru,*[3]" he said in Yoruba .

"I say, speak in English. *Olodo. Ko gbọ wa npa ọ in English.*[4]

When the boy said all this, Tayọ was so angry that he wanted to beat him up. Having thought about the implication of that, he left without saying anything further. As he was going, three schoolboys and a girl joined the boy. They started conversing in English. He overheard the boy telling the other students to join him and beat Tayo up. When he heard that, Tayo dropped his bin bag and ran. He heard them laughing at him. After that, he did not attempt to talk to any student again. Later that day when Mrs Aka and Tayọ got to Dugbẹ Market, they rushed over everything to beat the time to go to the pastor's place as planned.

"Tayọ, are you still okay for us to go and see the pastor?"

"Mummy, I am ready. I will like to find out the people that are after my life. That incident was scary but thank God, I survived it."

The pastor's church was about eight kilometres from the market. On their way, Tayọ was thinking about many things

he had seen or heard concerning pastors and prophecies. If
not for that fearful incident and its attendant nervousness,
he would have decided not to go and see any pastor for
prayer. He remembered very vividly what happened when
his grandmother once took him along to see a prophet
when he was still in the village. He was nicknamed
Dajọọku.[5] People from far and near revered him because if
he said somebody would die on a particular day, what was
left for such a person was to start preparing for the day he
would leave the world. Most often, such people would have
died psychologically before their foretold date of meeting
with death. To his followers, his pronouncement was
sacrosanct. This side of him made him a small god in their
locality. People who were sick or dreamed about death or
had any other life problems always ran to him for help. If he
said you would not die because of your sickness, you
needed to start rejoicing and call people for celebration of
the good news. Why everybody believed him baffled Tayọ
because quite a few people had died even when he told
them they would live. Whenever his grandfather asked him
to go with him to see Prophet *Dajọọku*, he always felt uneasy
because he would not like the prophet to tell him that he or
his grandfather or any member of his family would die on a
particular day.

One day both Tayọ and his grandmother went to the
prophet's holy ground to meet Dayọ. She came to the
secluded area in the forest for prayers and prophecies. It
was a last resort. Since the time she got married, she never

enjoyed her life. She was sick all the time. She became pregnant twice and, on each occasion, a caesarean section was performed on her. The two children still died at birth. She had gone to the orthodox and traditional hospitals for a solution but still, her problem persisted. Her husband had spent a lot on the sickness to the extent that his family members asked him to divorce her and get a healthy woman as wife. She told Grandmother that there was something in her womb. It was an object but it was hard to describe how it operated. That each time it moved, it left pains and scratches in her womb for weeks. She often fell sick, and at times she would not be able to eat, urinate or excrete for hours or days. She was x-rayed many times but nothing like what she described was found. The herbalists had advised her to go and beg her family to set her free as they were the ones behind her problems. She had made sacrifices to appease those she might have offended. Many times, when in pains, she had asked her grandparents to help her out. But all the same, the sickness persisted. Therefore, her coming to the prophet was to get a definite answer either positive or negative concerning her troubling situation. She had attempted to commit suicide when the pain became unbearable. Living became meaningless to her. It was on the advice of her grandmother that she came to find out what might be responsible for her difficulties.

However, what happened at the prophet's holy place made the day a memorable one for Tayọ. His thatched cottage roof was surrounded by white sand. Also outside, there were timber seats for visitors. Visitors were required to remove their shoes on arrival and had to queue to see the prophet. If you were in a hurry, you would need to come back some other day. Unless you are asked to, you must not say anything. No noise making. Babies were not welcomed because they might make a noise. Though they left their village very early, by the time they got there, many people were already in the queue. Each of them was given a number. That day Tayọ was excited to see Dayọ and receive some gifts from her but he was not ready to have any encounter with the prophet. He did not take the number given to him as he said he came with his grandmother. He saw the people and realised that life was full of problems. The prophet who was about to attend to one of his 'customers' saw Grandmother, came to her and greeted her. Why he did that, Tayọ did not know. While waiting, they watched the man praying and prophesying for each person he called to kneel in front of him.

It was once rumoured that if a person was troubled by evil people like witches and wizards, the prophet would name the witches and wizards even to their faces. Mostly, such people turned out to be close family members. For this, he was feared greatly. He was rumoured to accept to fast on behalf of troubled people if they were incapable of doing that on their own. He never asked for but received gifts from grateful people. To many people, he was doing the work of God and saving the lives of the people from the evil forces.

In the presence of everybody, the prophet directed the next person in the queue who happened to be a man to kneel for prayer. The man was the tenth person to be prayed for since Tayọ and his grandmother got there early that morning. Quickly, the man obeyed like a recruit accepting a general's last order. The man closed his eyes tightly, raised his open hands up to the sky and was shouting "Amen" as the prayer progressed. All other people opened their eyes, but they remained silent. Tayọ was looking at both the prophet and the man being prayed for with keen interest and awe.

"Jehova Jireeeeee. Ala ma ta Jeeeesu. Oooo Alleluuuuuuya Amen. Ramaaataaahaaashiiii. Glooooory Alleluuuuuuuya..."

The prophet uttered those seemingly meaningless words and phrases in a recurrent way. He jerked forward, backward, right and left with his Bible and the long thin white mace he was holding. At a point, he danced round the man several times and placed one hand on his head. Tayọ was enjoying the drama but at a time he whispered in his grandmother's ears, "Mama, what is wrong with both of them?"

"I know you will ask some questions. Nothing, just keep quiet. Have you started your naughtiness? I'll send you back to the village now if you're not careful," his grandmother said.

After some ten minutes of serious prayer, the prophet came round slowly and slowly. The place was as silent as a burial ground. He did not say anything for the first two minutes.

He closed his eyes and knelt down. Then, he stood up and shouted, *"Ho jah... Ho jah ah haaaa maaaaan*. All these are from the Living God. Hear o *maaaaan"*, the prophet began to shake violently and he was repeating one word many times. He continued, *"Ho a la ma ba ho Jeeesu mi tani oooo. Ọgbeni*[6], if you are not em...em....em....em....em....careful, *ho jaaaaah,* this year...... hear this, my son.....hear, hear, hear this clearly, you will surely be killed by one of your friends on a Saturday morning. You are already in his grip, *hoooo maaaan....* listen listeeen oh......would you be able to fast and pray?"

"Yes. Yes. Yes. Yes, Prophet. I will. I will. My God, thank you. *Mo dupẹ temi."*[7]

With that acceptance, the prophet knelt again and asked the man to shout *Alleluias* three times. The man stood up, jumped up and shouted three *Alleluias*. The prophet stood up and opened his eyes. He signalled to the man to move to the other side. Everybody was looking at the prophet with keen interest. Tayọ decided right there that he would not allow him to pray for him that day. He did not just want to be told that somebody had decided to kill him and that he would die unless he could pray and fast. The next man's case was also good. The prophet told him that some large sum of money was coming his way very soon. He was happy and people congratulated him on that. He left immediately. The next person was a woman. As she was kneeling, Tayọ saw his sister coming from afar. He left the gathering and ran to meet her. The first thing Tayọ told his sister after greetings was the case of the man who the prophet had prophesied would die on one Saturday morning if he failed to pray and fast that year. He pleaded with his sister not to let the prophet pray for her.

His sister who was looking unhealthy told him, "Stop the rubbish you're telling me. Is that the way to greet me? Why did Grandmother bring you along in the first instance? It would have been better if you were left in the village. Let's go but I don't want to hear a word from you till we finish, is that right?"

"Sorry, I won't talk again. You're welcome, did you bring anything for me?" She did not answer him as they walked to the Holy Ground and sat down quietly. When it was her turn, the prophet shook his head, looked up and down in a certain negative way which suggested he might have bad news for Dayọ. He beckoned to her to kneel. Next, the prophet called on her grandmother and Tayọ to join her. That had never happened before since Tayọ had been going to the Holy Ground. He at once feigned an excuse that he would like to go and relieve himself in the forest. His grandmother said he should not go but his sister and the prophet told him to go. He fled the place straight into the forest. He was there till the prayer came to an end.

"Stand up. Open your eyes and shout seven *Halleluiahs* to the Most High God," the prophet said.

At that point, Tayọ quickly ran back and sat beside other people on the bench to hear what the prophet would say to

his sister. No one took interest in his coming though.
Instead of saying something after the prayer, the prophet
kept quiet. He nodded and nodded for a long time with his
eyes closed. Dayọ and Grandmother were already feeling
uneasy and crying silently. Tayọ was confused as to what
that scene from the prophet meant.

*"I had told you not to allow him to pray for you. Now, you can
see,"* he was thinking.

A man who prophesied another person's death in Tayọ's
own understanding, must be a wicked fellow and a killjoy.
He had been taught in church that it is only God who could
make somebody live or die. . He wanted to tell the prophet
not to reveal what he had seen about his sister, but his
courage failed him. He noticed his grandmother and sister
were nervous. He was frightened.

"Um...... oh......*Jehova* God. Ah......this world and its people
are wicked," he began. He closed his eyes and shook his legs
where he sat. He shouted suddenly, "See, my daughter. Oh
Jeeeeeesu. Holy Mary...... please, see your daughter. My
daughter, your own relatives are behind your problems."
Grandmother was shocked and her countenance changed.
Tayọ and other people noticed this. Dayọ started crying
bitterly as she continued listening to the prophet.

"My daughter, it could have been easier to deal with your
problems if your problems came from those who are not
your relatives. But.... But....But people from your own very
house are your enemies....Oh.... Yes, your own family. Oh

wahahhamamamamaaaaahaaa." Grandmother nearly
touched the man to stop saying fearful things to her
granddaughter.

"An object like a yam tuber was planted in your womb when
you were still a baby by evil people and it has grown to
become a monster. You are not alone. You are not in this
alone. All your siblings from your mother are in the same
hot soup. Oh…. You are all in a cage. That's what I am
seeing. All of you, will however win the war. Oh…. Ah….
Um…. It is a war but all of you will suffer much before
victory comes your ways. Because…. Because…. It is from
your…. your…. your.... own relatives. *Jahmanaaaaacccceeee*."

Though Tayọ had expected the man to give the names of
those people who he said he was seeing, the prophet evaded
doing that. Each time it seemed he would name them; he
would stop short. The prophet stopped and kept quiet for
some minutes. He looked at Tayọ where he sat, pointed at
him and jokingly asked if he had got anything to say.

He said, "No. No. No sir." The prophet then dispersed them.

Back from his deep thought about what happened that day
at the prophet's Holy Ground, he heard mummy saying,
"Please driver, could you please drop us off at that next
junction."

When they came out from the taxi, they crossed to the
opposite side and walked to the church yard where the
pastor and his family lived. At the entrance to the yard, they

met the pastor's wife who informed Mrs Aka that her husband had been waiting for her. She apologised for their lateness. As they were about to be ushered into the pastor's prayer room, Tayọ was directed to wait in the living room. Mrs Aka went in to converse with the pastor. Barely some minutes later, Tayọ was invited to join them.

Looking straight at the pastor, he prostrated himself. The pastor greeted him warmly and said, "My child, kneel down and let us pray." He knelt and Mrs Aka joined him. The pastor prayed and both shouted "Amen" at the top of their voice. They sang and clapped their hands. At last, the pastor said, "In the name of the Father, the Son and the Holy Spirit."

"Amen. Amen. Amen," they responded.

"My son, stand up and shout seven great Hallelujah." He did that joyfully.

The pastor opened his eyes, smiled and said, "Sit down and listen carefully. You should continue to thank God. It's wonderful you survived what happened to you in your dream that night. Yes. Wonderful. The name of the Lord must be praised for that."

"Thank God. Thank God. Thank God," Mummy said.

"The man you saw in your dream with the pot containing hot water represented the head of those who have decided to work against your destiny. They were agents of the devil. They determined to get rid of you. The pot he was carrying contained combined problems they wanted to give you. Individually, each had tried to eliminate you, to make you suffer and sad, but your God failed them. That's why they sent their 'Goliath' to come and finish you off. Shout Hallelujah." Both Mrs Aka and Tayọ stood up and shouted Hallelujah three times.

"My little child," the pastor continued, "those devil-incarnates met and decided to end it all for you through their combined efforts but they did not know that your God neither slumbers nor sleeps. They were all waiting in their camp to hear the bad news about you at that point in time. But thank God, you woke up before the pot with the hot water hit you. If it had struck you when you were still sleeping and helpless, you would have been a dead person by now. That was why when you woke up, you felt some burning like fire within you. Frankly speaking, it was more than fire. It was our God that rendered the impact powerless."

As the pastor continued with his revelation, Tayọ closed his eyes, placed his hands on his head and started shaking. The pastor embraced and comforted him saying, "Don't worry too much my son. The fact that you're still alive till this moment means God wants to do something special in your life or use you to show how mighty He is over the forces of evil. As Mummy can testify, all of us face different problems all the time, including myself, Christians and non-Christians. But when we place our faith in God, we become overcomers. Before you start in your high school, I'll give you some verses in the Book of Psalm that you will need to read into your life every day. Hope you hear me well. Every day. That will settle the case. How about that?"

"That will be very good for me sir. I will do that sir," Tayọ said.

"Good. The evil people have turned their devilish plan on their head because they failed in their satanic mission, and sooner, they will be exposed," said the pastor.

Mrs Aka could not believe how a small boy of Tayọ's age could have gathered up such a large number of enemies.

"As a warning," the pastor continued, "though you have won this battle, make sure you stay away as much as possible from trouble. I can see you're a man of destiny but that's the more reason you must start behaving as one. Watch and pray. Don't fight with your fellow students. I say it again, be prayerful and always believe that things shall work out for you positively. Don't let what happened put unnecessary fear in you as I've earlier said. You shall overcome. May the good Lord keep, protect and bless you."

"Amen, Amen and Amen," both Tayọ and Mrs Aka responded.

Mrs Aka knelt again on behalf of Tayọ and thanked the pastor. On their way home, Tayọ was very happy that at least, the pastor had not prophesied doom regarding his situation.

"So, Pastors have problems too, why? he asked himself.

Inside the taxi, Mrs Aka advised him to abide by everything the pastor had told him. He thanked her and promised to keep to the warnings.

CHAPTER EIGHT

Do *not let the behaviour of others destroy your inner peace* - Dalai Lama

The following Sunday after the visit to the pastor's place, Tayọ was given the permission to go and visit his father and explain to him all that had happened. He woke up very early as usual and did all the usual house duties. After breakfast, he bade the family of Mrs Aka goodbye and set out for his father's workplace. It was still the same company where Tayọ had worked few months before. He had developed a liking for his father despite the way he had treated him in the past. He could still not understand why his father's behaviour to him changed drastically once he moved to the city. Immediately he alighted from the bus, he saw his father opening the gate for a vehicle leaving the company premises. He was happy that he was working that day as he used to work from Monday to Saturday. He greeted his father. His welcoming attitude showed that he was happy to see him.

"Tayọ, you're welcome. Are you fine? Why are you here today?" his father asked.

His tone was not as harsh as it used to be. His utterances in the past were part of what led him to become a house help. He remembered also that when his uncle that got him the job told his father about it, he was not all that bothered. He believed he had refused to accept his fatherly advice and because of that he left him to please himself as he had once threatened. After some minutes, he explained the purpose of his visit to his dad. Before he could tell him about their visit to the pastor, his father jocularly called him a cowardly boy.

"You shouldn't have opened your eyes. You should have fought the evil man to a standstill. I know you my son, you're very tough."

"But I told you the man was horrible and unsightly. His appearance was like that of the Biblical Goliath but uglier."

"That being the case, you too should have fought him like the Biblical David or have you forgotten his story?"

"Bàba, this is a serious issue that even landed me in the hospital. This isn't a joke at all. If not for the care given to me in the hospital paid for by Mrs Aka and her family, maybe I should be dead by now."

"It must have been very serious then. Could you tell me in detail what happened?"

He mustered enough courage to remember some of what happened that night and told his father how he slept after his usual busy day. He told him about the dream, how he woke up sweating and felt he was being burnt by fire, how he was rushed to the hospital by the kind-hearted Mrs Aka and her family, the visit to the pastor's place and his revelations. He told his father the pastor warned him to stay away from any form of trouble all the time. "I pray God will help me to do this though I know I'm not troublesome." As he said that, his father listened to him attentively and felt sorry for him for going through all that as young as he was.

"My son, I'm happy you escaped unhurt and alive to tell your story. This life is full of evil people who are always ready to harm others. But as Mrs Aka and the pastor correctly told you, it is only God that can protect someone from the evil people. As you survived that terrible attack, God will continue to protect you."

"Amen. Thank you, daddy."

"When are you going back and when are you starting your new school?"

"I am going back today but schools will not resume until September."

"That is good. What do you want to eat?"

"Nothing. I ate some food before I came here. I'm still okay."

"Lest I forget, tell Mrs Aka that I would come and pay her family a visit very soon to thank them for the support and care for you since you moved into their home. God will reward them handsomely."

He was happy that without asking his father to come and show appreciation to Mrs Aka's family, he offered to do so. His behaviour to him that day was a pleasant surprise. Tayo reemphasised the roles played by Mrs Aka's family especially that of uncle Dele and told his father to remember to thank him for that. He let his father know about some things he would need in preparation for high school but assured him not to fret, as he had been saving his monthly wages to take care of many of those things. He asked his father if he had heard that the incoming government in their region had promised to make education free and compulsory from primary to tertiary level.

"Yes, my son. I was very happy to hear the good news. I pray the Lord help that political party and its leaders. It has not always been easy for poor people like me with many children to send our children to school. I am happy that at last, you will go to high school as you have dreamed about all your life. Congratulations," his father patted him on the back. "But I want to advise you to work very hard, much more than you did in primary school to come out successful. You now know that life is an opportunity. As young as you are, you have seen suffering which often teaches people serious lessons. Don't join gangs. Go to school punctually and regularly. Respect your teachers and follow their instructions. They are in the school to shape your life and give you a bright future. Don't steal. Be content with whatever that is yours. Many students nowadays have become thugs and thieves. Please, don't be numbered among them. You know me, I don't have money as I used to, but I am still working hard to make both ends meet. If you follow what I'm telling you today, your tomorrow will be far better than mine."

"Thank you. I will try. That's what everyone has been telling me. Please, be praying for me so that the evil people you talked about will not trouble me anymore. I know one day I will become somebody important like your company director and I will help you."

"Amen, so shall it be. We hope the incoming government will fulfil its promises which will surely make people's lives better and help our future generations to become well educated and help us their parents."

As both were talking in his father's security guard cubicle, everyone who had not seen Tayọ for some time was asking him if he was enjoying his job. He joyfully told them he was. It showed on him though as he was looking smart and well fed. Some of his *meija-meiload* friends told him his father had informed them that he had got admission into a high school. He proudly told them it was true and that very soon, he would further his education. He was respected in a place where some months prior to that visit, he was being vilified by everybody who thought he was arrogant and foolish for refusing to do what his father asked him to do. When their discussion came to an end, his father asked him if he could help him wash some of his dirty clothes before going back to Mrs Aka's place. Without waiting for his response, his father asked him to come with him to his rented room to do the washing. He told his colleagues that if the director asked of him, they should tell him that he had taken his son to know where he was living. They got to the place a few minutes later and it was a very dirty house. There was no kitchen, but it had toilet and bathroom at least. Tayo's mind went straight back to Mr and Mrs Aka's shining beautiful flat. He figured out that the cause of the glaring differences between his family and Mrs Aka's family's living condition was the fact that his father married many wives and had many children. He believed his father had bitten off more than he could chew. The difference between the two families was much.

"*Baba*, isn't this place too dirty and too small to live in? Isn't it possible for you to get a bigger room in a more decent environment?"

"Look Tayọ, that's part of what I was telling you earlier on. I don't have much money anymore. Paying for this small place is quite difficult but it is still better than when I used to sleep in the open at my workplace because I could not afford a room. I work 12 hours a day, six days a week, but I still find it difficult to take care of my family. The meagre salary I earn hardly sustains us for the whole month. I'll like to live in a better place like some other people but 'without money,' as they often say, 'there is no man.'"

After listening to his father's philosophical response, he managed to hold his tears. He was enveloped with anguish.

"You don't need to feel bad Tayọ. Work very hard at this young age so that when you grow up, you will live and enjoy better than I do now. Do you understand this?"

"Yes father."

His father brought out the dirty clothes for him to wash. The strength to wash them had left him because he was sad about what he heard and saw that day. His father was about to go back to work when he saw his third wife coming with her little child strapped to her back while holding another two.

"Oh. This woman again. She's here with her trouble. Trouble all the time. In fact, I'm tired," Tayọ's father said to himself.

Tayọ who was not aware of anything, looked up to see why his father was talking to himself. Few metres to where he was washing the clothes, he saw his father's wife coming. He did not expect to meet with any of his father's wives there. Her appearance was disgusting, and her eyes were as red as fire. Her children looked sickly. Tayọ knew that she had come for a fight with her husband. He greeted her but she did not reply.

"Mama Ṣogo, welcome," he said very politely.

"Please don't ever greet me."

"Good day to you my wife," her husband said.

"Father and son, I don't need your greetings. What's good in the day in the first place? No money. No food for myself and my children? You, Tayọ, go and greet your runaway and good-for-nothing mother, don't bother to greet me."

Before he could think of anything to say, his father said, "Why do you always look for trouble this woman? Is it wrong for me and my son to greet you? Anyway, what has Tayọ done wrong just now? Hum…. Ok, my children come and greet me. Don't mind your mother."

"If any of you move from here, I'll give you hard knocks on your head. If he doesn't take care of you, why should I allow him to behave to you as if he is a good father. No way."

"You're telling my own children not to greet me. You're telling my children in my presence that I'm a bad father? This is serious. When will you change your wrong attitude?"

"I don't know for you. Once you're ready to change and perform your fatherly role, I will," she replied.

"But am I not doing my best? If you asked for money and I couldn't give you the exact amount you wanted, I often managed to give you some. Isn't this the truth?" Tayọ kept quiet but later he asked his half-brother to come and greet him. As the little boy turned towards him, his mother, who had started shouting at her husband, looked back and said, "Ṣogo, come back here now. Don't let him touch you. His mother and grandmother are witches." As she said this, the innocent boy turned back and ran to his mother. Tayọ was about to speak out when his father said,

"I've said it several times. You are a very troublesome woman. If not, no matter what happens between the two of us, you should not bring our children into it. I love my children and I am doing my best for them. If you're not happy with my effort, I won't kill myself and I won't go and steal. No. If you say I've offended you, fine. But, what has Tayọ done to deserve all these horrible comments? Also, and I ask again, why should you stop my children from greeting me?"

"It is because you are not a good husband. That I know for sure."

"Now, I'm no more a good husband but when everything was going fine with me, when my business was doing well, I was a good husband. That aside, you said Tayọ's mother and grandmother are witches. If truly they are, they should have used their witchcraft powers to kill you or render you insane long time ago. Don't you know that?"

"I know you will always support your son, his mother and grandmother because they've poisoned your mind. That's why you married a witch and you don't even know. Like father, like son." She retied her boubou and locked up horns with her husband. By this time, a crowd had collected. Their family became an object of ridicule within a very short time.

"If you fail to leave my shirt and stop your acerbic utterances, I'll teach you how not to be rude to your husband even if he doesn't have a penny. Money or no money, a cultured wife should have some respect for her husband."

As the two of them were exchanging hot words, her two children began to cry. Tayọ looked at them and shed tears too. As he and one elderly onlooker tried to take his father away from her, she gave Tayọ a slap and told him to back off. As her blow landed on Tayọ's face, his father gave her two in return. She fell flat on the floor. She did not expect the slaps. She first kept quiet before she started crying. She shouted, "*O ti pami o.*[1] Everyone, come and see this useless man that wants to kill me because of his useless son."

Her husband was so annoyed that he wanted to kick her but the peacemakers and Tayọ prevented him from doing that. They begged him to leave her as they took him away from the ugly scene. Though some believed her husband shouldn't have beaten her; others thought that she deserved what she got for slapping an innocent boy in his father's presence.

"Please, Baba Ṣogo, that is enough for today. May we not use our own hands to bring problem upon our own head," an elderly neighbour appealed to him.

"Why don't you let me kill her and kill myself? She is not normal. She is just too troublesome. In fact, my wives are evil. No peace from any one of them. They want to kill me but before that happens, I will show them one by one that enough is enough. There are other men with five or six wives all over the place. They do have some rest of mind and peace in their homes. But I married horrible ones without knowing it."

As he said that, Tayọ was thinking, "*My father forgot that by marrying many wives, he invited bitter rivalry into his own family especially as he does not have enough money again to look after them. Those men with many wives he refers to must have been good human managers considering daily strife among their competing women. One wife, one trouble it is.*"

"Eh....eh....eh....eh, he has killed me because of his stupid son," she continued to shout in tears.

She recounted her tales of woes to everyone all over and said, "God will punish you. My children are sick and I asked you for money to treat them but you refused to give me any money. For the past one month I have been pestering you. You take care of other wives and their children. Hear this Táyọ̀, you, your sisters and your mother will pay for this ugly treatment your father has meted to me. I will show all of you hell. We're just starting."

"How could this woman shift all the blame on me and my sisters, for God's sake? Why did I even come here today? Does she even know how much we suffer? Has my father been taking care of any of us? How I wish this woman could understand the situation of things between us and him. This is real trouble. Could she be one of those who wanted to get rid of me? Will she bewitch us as she has vowed? Could this happen to me if my mother was here? Why did my father marry all these women? I'll not even marry when I grow up to avoid all this trouble. No one knows where the shoe pinches but the one who wears one," Tayọ kept agonising as he was sure his father was feeling the pinches where they hurt most.

When Mama Ṣogo refused all entreaties to come back later for the money, her husband was advised to borrow some money from neighbours to give her to give peace a chance. At first, he refused but after a second thought, he got some money and gave it to her. She complainingly took the money and left. Tayọ felt ashamed that his father had to borrow to take care of his family. He compared his father's situation with that of Mr and Mrs Aka and felt bad. He wondered if marrying one wife could be the answer to avoid a house of commotion but again, he had seen some instances where marital monogamy had not produced a desired peaceful home.

"Those whose marriages are working properly should be given kudos. It's hard work. How do they do it? Hum...." he thought to himself.

He could not finish washing his father's clothes because of the uproar his wife had caused. When they were going back to his father's workplace, he told his father, "I can see where my problem came from now. Daddy, don't you think that Mama Ṣogo is one of the evil people trying to get rid of me? I'm in a serious trouble. I'm so afraid now."

"Don't worry. She can't do you any harm. If she is as powerful and wicked as she is claiming to be, all of us should have been dead. Let me give you this piece of advice. When you grow up, pray to God to give you a wife that will love you from the bottom of her heart. And once your prayer is answered, stick with her like glue. Marital journey is most of the time rough because of those who make up the marriage. Women are necessary evil. I'm not saying men are angels either, don't get me wrong. My wives wrecked me and made me an object of shame in the community. I once had money, strength and honour. All those things left me because of the never-ending-matrimonial war in my family which brought me shame. My son, I've seen troubles from women many times. Marital excursion is like climbing a staircase, as united couples are going up with strength and joy, disagreeable couples are pushing themselves down the stairs with terrible consequences. In my case, I stumbled down from the staircase when I got to the middle. Before this week runs out, another one of them will come with her own problems.

"At first, my wives were my ego booster but later, they turned out to be wolves in sheep clothing. It is hard to satisfy one wife not to talk of two or more of them if you're not loaded with cash. From my own experience and from what I have observed so far, marrying many wives is an ill wind that blows nobody any good. Your mother left all of us after she had done her worst. Tell me, was what she did right?" Before he could reply, his father continued with his *Sermon on the Mount*, "You are growing up fast, learn from my own downfall."

"Hum…. I will. God will help me. But one more thing, why did you slap Mama Ṣogo back?"

"Why did you ask that question?"

"Hum…. em…. em…. I just want to know."

"Well, what she did was wrong. She shouldn't have slapped you because you were not at all involved in our argument. You were only trying to calm the two of us down which was good of you. Moreover, I was angry and if anyone had done that to her child, I would have acted the same way. I hate people maltreating children. People can discipline them if they do anything wrong. I'm not against that, but treating children badly is what I hate. Have you ever seen me beating any of my wives before?"

"No, I can't remember. That's what surprised me."

"Sorry if I have hurt you."

"Well…. em…. em…. Anger is bad then," he quipped.

"That's correct my son but...but....at times, it's difficult to control our anger. Have you never got angry?"

"Yes…. I have at times….Hum…."

When the father and the son ended their question-and-answer session, Tayọ pitied his father the more because of all he had gone through. Even though he and his sisters had suffered hardship since childhood because of their parents' absence in their upbringing, he still loved his father because he owned up to his mistakes and he believed he was an intelligent man. He believed that if he had had a second chance, maybe things might have played out differently for him. He stayed for some hours with him and he enjoyed his father's company for the first time in a long time. But his father's wife's erratic behaviour in the public that day haunted Tayọ for a long time. When it was time for him to leave, both of them felt unhappy.

"Tayọ, should I give you some money for transport back to your place? I have some little money with me."

"Don't worry Daddy. Mummy gave me enough money. She is very generous as I told you earlier."

"God bless her, she's doing what all of us should learn to do, help anyone we can help irrespective of whom they are. Extend my greetings to her. I pray her own children will meet helpers where they do not even expect. It is good to be good."

"I will need to go back now as Mummy gave me a specific time to get back home. When I come back home to start school, we will be seeing more of each other. But, don't forget to come as soon as possible to see her and her family as you have promised. I think they deserve it. Goodbye."

"No, I will not forget at all. Goodbye my son."

Tayọ almost cried leaving his father that day. Where the sudden attachment between his father and him came from, he did not know.

On his way back, he went to see the woman who was helping him to keep his monthly wages. He informed her of his success in the common entrance examination and that he would soon need the money to pay his first school fees in case nobody picked the bill before the incoming government would be sworn in and start to pay school fees for all students. The woman was very happy to hear that he was successful. He left with the assurance from her that his money was intact and ready for his use at any time. On the bus on his way back, he was lost in thought. He thought again about what had just happened in his father's rented house and his father's candid advice and hoped they would help him later.

"I think my daddy blindly brought avoidable problems on himself. Mama Ṣogo said my mother and my grandmother are witches. Could she be right? No. Never. I can't believe that nonsense. My grandmother couldn't have been a witch. Not at all. If she were to be one, I would have been dead and gone back to my Creator long

time ago. She said we would suffer for life. Since there is no one to fight on our behalf, please God, protect us, we're your children."

The more he tried to be happy, the more many of his family circumstances and his environment made him unhappy. His happiness mostly came from his 'adoptive family' which Mrs Aka's family had become. Any time he was alone, he pondered over his unique problems like a widow deserted by family and friends at her hour of need.

CHAPTER NINE

et today be the start of something new - Arjun Nagella
When Tayọ got back to Mrs Aka's place, she
asked, "What was your father's thought about
what happened to you that night in your dream?"

He explained how his father felt and told them of his
father's appreciation for all they were doing for him. He
informed them that his father promised to come personally
to thank them.

"So, thank God everything went well between you and your
father," she said.

"Yes ma. I thank God."

He did not say a word about the ugly incident between his
father and Mama Ṣogo. He thought telling them would

bring him shame. He wondered if they would understand fully how terrible the situation in his family was. He told them his father assured him not to be afraid and that God would protect him all the time. As he knew that he would soon leave Mrs Aka and her family, he worked like never before to show them that he really appreciated all they had done for him. He also believed that doing that would make them welcome him with open hands any time he came back for a visit. The night before he went back to his family house was very emotional for everyone present.

The next day, which was a Sunday, he woke up early and did all he was supposed to do very quickly. That morning's family devotion was dedicated to him.

"Could all of us be on our feet and in a circle," Mrs Aka directed. Everyone obeyed.

"Tayọ, come right here in this circle and kneel down. Could we all close our eyes, point our hands towards Tayọ and pray aloud on his behalf that God should be with him, protect him, make him successful and be favoured wherever he turns to." The family prayed aloud unlike never before.

"Amen. Amen. Amen. Amen. Amen….," Tayọ was saying aloud as the heavenly blessings were being rained on him.

When that session ended, Mrs Aka said, "First, our God and our dear Father we thank You for a day like this. Today is a very special day in this family. We all know why. One, this boy came here to work for us. He arrived here safely and he is going back safely. Two, through the support we gave to him as a family and his own hardworking spirit, he sat the common entrance exam and passed. Three, we did not send or ask his family to come and collect his dead body because of what happened in his sleep that night. For these and many more, we thank You our Lord Jesus."

"Thank You Jesus," everybody chorused.

"Tayọ, as you are going into the world, the Lord will go with you. Whenever we shall be hearing from you, it will always be good news. Continue to be a good boy and you'll reap the reward one day. I tell you, there's nothing bad in being good. Study well. Becoming academically successful takes much time and effort. Obey your teachers and your parents. Don't join bad gangs that will corrupt you and lead you astray. Don't leave God out of your life plan. Hold on to Him. Call on Him privately and publicly. He is a good Father; He will not fail you. More trying times will still come your way, but never give up. It is what all of us must experience at one time or the other. As you are leaving us, we're not leaving you. In spirit, we will continue to ask God to help you. You will be the head and not the tail." Before she ended her exhortation, Tayọ was spiritually moved. It was something he had never experienced before.

"Thank you Mummy. You've been there for me. God will continue to be there for you. God will continue to bless you ma."

"It's a pleasure, it's been good knowing you. Ķǫlá, go to your room and bring our family gift for your friend."

Ķǫlá quickly went to his room and came back with a big bag full of gifts. They had kept it as a secret. Mrs Aka opened the bag and one by one, she brought out all its content. They were various items for which any student going to high school would be grateful. Tayǫ was speechless. He prostrated himself and thanked the family for the amazing gifts and the emotional support they had given him till that day.

"Thank you, Daddy. Thank you, Mummy. Uncle Dele, thank you very much. My sisters and Ķǫlá, I can't thank you enough. My God will thank you on my behalf. My father will come and thank you too. I don't know what to say again but please, always pray for me as you have promised."

"You are welcome. We will do that. You are such a lovely boy. Keep it up. And don't forget you once told me that you would come to the University of Ibadan to study when you finish your high school. Work very hard to make that a reality. You can do it," Dele said.

"I will and God will help me. Thank you for reminding me, sir."

"Tayǫ, this small envelope is for you. There's 85-naira in it. This is our own small contribution towards your education. Use the money wisely. Don't stop your education at high school level. Have it at the back of your mind from the outset that you will come back to our university as a student as Dele has just said. Will you? My family and I will be very proud of that achievement."

"Yes ma, I will do all my best to make sure this happens. Mummy, thank you ma. Thank you. I'm very grateful," he said with tears rolling down his cheeks.

"These are tears of joy. We can understand. We're all going to church very soon. I will ask one of our pastors to pray for you when we finish the service. When we come back from church, Dele and Kọlá will accompany you home. They will know your family house from where you will be going to school."

"They don't need to do that Mummy, I can go back home alone," he said that because he feared what they might think of the area of the city where his family house was located. Despite his opinion, Dele and Kọlá took him home in the family car. On the way, he planned to take them straight to Uncle Sunday's house in their neighbourhood. His house, though located in the same neighbourhood, was somehow presentable. They parked their car on the road as Tayọ's area had no streets that led to every home unlike what operated in Mrs Aka's area of the city. Dele and Kọlá covered their noses because of the smell coming from the gutters, they walked carefully to avoid falling into the drain as some did when they were not watchful enough.

"Uncle Dele, you can see why I said you should not worry to come and drop me off at home. It's because of this sort of area where I live. No planning, no maintenance of anything in our area," Tayọ said.

"That's no problem at all Tayọ. Don't worry," Dele said.

Luckily for him, Uncle Sunday was at home. He welcomed Mrs Aka's children and thanked them profusely for all they did for Tayọ in the short time he worked for them. He wanted to entertain them but they politely declined his offer.

Thus, he left Mrs Aka's family with much love and celebration but with some mixed feelings about his own future.

The new school term was a glorious dawn for Tayọ as his long-term dream had come to reality. Just like the day he started primary school, he woke up very early, took his bath, ate and left for school. He looked like a real student in his new school uniform, school shoes and new school bag bought for him by Mrs Aka's family. Seeing him for the first time, he might have been mistaken for a schoolboy from an affluent family.

His new school, Origbo High School, was situated in the core part of Ibadan City. It was once privately owned before a military government took it over by fiat from its owner. It was not a big high school. The student population was mainly from that community of peasants and semi-educated strugglers. Other well-known schools in the city hardly wanted to have anything to do with the school except that by law, all schools were connected to one another. It was a mixed school. The school looked beautiful, but its location was a minus. There was no designated playing area for sports where students could do exercise. Students did some exercise on a very limited land area close to the assembly ground. For football, it could only be 6-aside match and that was if volleyball match was not going on. One must give way for the other. Accordingly, if the inter-house sports competition was taking place, the practice and the real events needed to be carried out at one of the bigger nearby grammar schools. There was no farmland to teach practical agriculture either.

Some of those important school facilities which the school did not have opened it and its students to jest and dressing down from other well-equipped schools dotted all over the ancient city. In fact, the whole Origbo High School was just another school's standard football field in size. However, the school had many qualified teachers who could measure up to other teachers in the bigger and well-known schools.

Tayọ's family house was not far from the school. So, he was not entitled to join the school bus to and from home. His consolation was that those of them who excelled in sports and academics were often driven on the bus to venues of school events. He scarcely missed any. When he further made enquiry about how the bus service was being run, he was informed that all students who used the bus paid for it. With that information, he knew he could not use the bus in the way he had thought he would.

At the assembly hall that morning, all new Form 1 students were asked to be on two lines. After that, they were re-grouped into three class arms, each arm consisted of thirty students. They were assigned to Class 1A, 1B and 1C. The principal welcomed them and told all of them important pieces of information.

He said, "Discipline is vital to learning. Respect for the teaching, non-teaching staff and senior students will be required from you all the time. Regular attendance and punctuality are very important for all students. Our school is education and sports focused. We will do our best to develop you and make you useful to yourself, your family and the society. We know this is not an easy task but it is achievable. With all these pieces of information which you will continue to be reminded of every time, you are welcome to this great school where students are moulded to become greater tomorrow and captains of industries and political leaders. Your class teachers will take you through other school protocols carefully, I wish you all the best of luck."

With that expression of goodwill, Mr Ṣalakọ, the school principal, rounded off that morning's assembly. Students sang the Nigerian National Anthem followed by the Pledge and then marched to their classes. Tayọ was placed in Form 1B. Their class teacher went to their class immediately after the assembly and emphasised what the principal had told them.

"We have some rules and regulations governing the running of this school and classes as you have heard from the principal. But it is still very important I run over them and add some," Mr Aliu, his class teacher began. "You must all come to school punctually and regularly. Do not steal, tell lies or speak in vernacular, that is, in your native language unless during a class for such a language. Noise making, immoral activities, bullying, use of abusive language and lack of respect for our school staff and senior students are forbidden. Anyone of you who goes against any of these rules would be dealt with accordingly. You are no more primary school pupils. From now, start working very hard in your studies. Don't leave till tomorrow what you can do today. Maybe you believe it or not, your five years' stay in this school will soon come to an end and your final result will have serious implications for your educational advancement.

"As usual, all your school fees receipts will be checked. Debtors will be sent back home until they pay what they owe the school. Once the new regional government is sworn in and free and compulsory education is introduced, fees of any kind will no more be collected. We will carefully follow government directives on how we run the school. Your personal hygiene is very important. Take good care of it. Dress smartly and don't tarnish the image of this school outside."

After this, Mr Aliu took the register. Tayọ came to realize that secondary school's life was quite different from that of primary school. Normal school activities started at quarter-to-eight in the morning for all students. The punctuality prefect would be at the school's main gate by seven-thirty. The duty teacher would also be somewhere monitoring how students conducted themselves. Students would troop in from all the roads that led to the school. At ten to eight, students would pick up the litter around the school premises. At eight, they would be in the assembly hall. Any student who arrived late would either be caned or asked to cut a section of grass after school hours. Often, some prefects would ask late comers to frog-jump to their classes. By the time they finished, they would be begging for breath. Many students because of that form of punishment learned the hard way to come to school on time.

In high school, senior students often punished junior students for failure to comb their hair, tuck in their shirts, greet or respect them within and outside the school premises. If a junior student refused to go on an errand for them especially in the school premises, for example, such a student would be punished. Any attempt made to report such a senior student to the teachers often led to harsher punishment from the senior's mates. Most junior students therefore suffered in silence at the hands of the overindulged seniors as the fear of them was the beginning of high school wisdom. Though most of Tayọ's age mates were in senior classes, he did not allow that to disturb him. He knew that everyone would get to their destinations at different times in life.

One morning, Mr Aliu came to the class to mark the register. After he had finished doing that, he said, "Today, we want to appoint a class monitor who will be the one to make sure this class runs smoothly. He will work hand in hand with me on day-to-day basis so we can get the desired cooperation from all of you for proper education to take place. For example, he could ask the whole class to tidy up this classroom. He may be asked to take register, collect assignment, report noise makers and do some other duties as assigned to him by me. This is an important post with added responsibilities. Could any of you volunteer to be this class monitor?" Nobody signified. All kept quiet.

"In the absence of a volunteer, we need a nomination."

"Excuse me sir, I nominate this boy, Tayọ Kọlapọ," Ṣina, a lousy boy, shouted from the back of the class.

"Will Tayọ please stand up for recognition?"

"Sorry sir, I am not interested," he told the class teacher.

"That's okay Tayọ but remain standing for now. Any other nomination?" the teacher asked.

"No sir," the whole class shouted.

Tayọ was dumbfounded. He rejected the offer not because he was not interested but because of his usual insecurity. He put up courage, left his seat and went to the class teacher to tell him silently why he did not want the position.

"Sir, please, I don't think I'm capable of doing some of the things you've talked about. Some students in this class can ridicule you especially when you make any mistake in your grammar. I've noticed that when a teacher is in the class, it's ok but once the teacher leaves, it's the other way round. They will remember your mistakes and laugh at you."

The teacher patted him on the back, led him out of the class to the passage and gently told him, "Tayọ, you're a very courageous boy. I can see that in you. You are here to learn, aren't you?" Tayọ nodded.

"That being the case," the teacher continued, "remember, one learns to write by writing and one learns to speak by speaking. I have seen that you have a very legible handwriting and you communicate well through your writing. No problem in that area. Your spoken English is not bad because I have seen worse cases before. You will need to work more on your speaking skills in English and be more confident. That's what all of you will have to do from now till you leave this school. Mind you, all of you will continue to improve on that. You should know that fingers are not equal. Some of your classmates can speak so well but they may not be able to write so well. At the same time, some can write so well but they might be timid speakers.

Don't always feel offended whenever you make mistakes and some of them laugh at you. Though that won't be tolerated, it's all part of learning and adjusting. Everyone makes mistakes in speaking or writing. I know it's hard but you can do it. Is that okay with you?"

"Thank you, sir. It is okay with me. I'll try to do more on that as you've said."

When the two came back into the class, the teacher asked the class to clap for Tayọ because he had agreed to be the class monitor. He thanked his teacher and left for his seat having been given the insignia of office as the class captain. He took the post of the class monitor as a challenge and he put all that the teacher told him into practice. In a short time, he began to speak confidently in simple and correct English and in the end, Tayọ overcame his glossophobia. Initially, some *ajẹbọta*[1] students would make sure they look for mistakes in whatever he said. Few of those *ajẹbọtà* students that came to Origbo High School to study were there not by choice. They were in the school because they could not get admission to well-known high schools due to poor results in their common entrance or because of other problems. They would laugh whenever Tayọ or any other local students made grammatical mistakes. They were quick to spot errors because they attended good kindergarten, nursery and primary schools. Most of them would not normally finish their education in Origbo High School as their parents often transferred them out from there to other good schools in the city. The irony of it was that they made some students who were in the same league as Tayọ to keep quiet in class in order for them not to be humiliated. A female student in the class once said, "I wented and buyed my books at the bookshop yesterday." She was ridiculed to the extent that she was nicknamed 'wented and buyed' by the *ajẹbọta* clique. The class teacher reprimanded the gang while the other so-called local students supported the girl.

Tayọ, considering what was happening in his class, beat the *ajẹbọta* students at their own game. How did he do this? Mr Aliu asked him to come to the staff room during the break time one day. He went to see him. After some discussion about Tayọ's study progress, his teacher gave him some short and interesting novels to read at home, in addition to the ones being read in the school. He told him to start to listen actively to news broadcast and watch some television programmes and pay close attention to how the newsreaders and programme presenters worked. In addition to that, he asked him to get a notebook where he would write new words and new interesting phrases, idioms and proverbs that he might come across. He advised him to look up meanings of such new words, phrases idioms and proverbs in the dictionary and add them to his own vocabulary. He told him to start reading newspapers and magazines.

"Tayọ, do all these and you'll have good story to tell soon. Feel free to come to me or any other teacher to explain anything to you which may be out of your depth. Don't be shy. Teachers love students who do extra work and come to them for further discussion on some subject areas they might be finding difficult."

"Thank you, sir. That's interesting, I'll do as you've said."

Tayọ did with diligence those things his teacher advised him to do. Within months, he had become a changed boy. He started to speak confidently in class. The *ajẹbọta* students were surprised. One of them said one day in the class during a free period, "Immediately I washed my uniform, I hanged it to dry."

Tayọ told him politely, "Wait a minute and please don't be offended, *hanged* was not the right tense to use in that sentence."

"What's the right tense, *Mr Grammarian?*"

Tayọ explained to him as other students looked on with rapt attention, *"hang* can have *hung hung* as the past and past participle and at the same time, it can have *hanged hanged* as its past and past participle. Depending on what you mean, the past and the past participle will change accordingly. If you can look up the word in the dictionary and read all the explanations provided, you'll understand what I'm trying to say. I can't say anything further, understanding English tenses is somehow complex."

"Mr Grammar, well done," one of the students shouted.

Since that time, all his classmates started giving him due respect. Some would tease him by calling him *grammarian*

all the time. That incident encouraged him to do more
research on the use of English. He saturated his brain with
English lexis. Whenever he pronounced any big word like
egalitarian, ombudsman, revolutionary, sceptical, pathetically,
simplicity, gargantuan or *anachronistic* and explained what
each word meant, his haters would quickly look the word
up in the dictionary to be sure he was not speaking Latin.
They became envious of him as they did not know how he
changed from being a timid boy to becoming a self-
confident student bombarding them with English words
many of them had never heard before. Subject teachers
developed a liking for him because his reasoning in the class
surpassed their expectations. He became the class
representative during the school inter-class literary and
debating competition. At last, he eliminated his stage fright
once his command of English had improved tremendously.
This helped him to perform well in other subjects too.

Tayọ tried to find out the academic performances of his
mates, especially those of the *ajẹbọta* students in class work
and examinations to see if for certain they were better off.
Before he came to the city to start high school, he believed
that it was only those students in the city who attended
good nursery and primary schools and had good command
of the English language that would normally do better than
the rest of them who did not have those opportunities. To
his greatest astonishment, many of them from very poor
background outperformed those they had regarded as
'eggheads'. Whereas many of them could speak like the

Queen of England, they often found it difficult to write what they spoke. It was then he learned that spoken and written English were quite different though one may help the other. In the first term examination, he came third out of thirty students in his class. It was a tough competition unlike in the primary school where the first or second position was his birth right. He was promoted to Form 2 and he found out that the class was not easy. It was a case of the higher you go, the tougher it becomes. Some of his friends failed the sessional examination and they were asked to repeat.

From Form 1 to Form 3, school life was fun for Ṭayọ, he was full of vigour and sociability. Seniority was a basic idea in his school as earlier mentioned. A junior student must respect his/her seniors and call them 'Senior John', 'Senior Maryam' or Senior Ṣẹgun even if John, Maryam or Ṣẹgun was few years younger than the junior student. You might be an older student in Form 1 but you needed to call a younger student in Form 2, 3, 4 or 5 'Senior so and so'. It was a well-established school custom.

Senior Abẹki was a tall, huge and handsome male student. He was in Form 5 and Ṭayọ was in Form 3. The senior attracted the ladies in his school as ants to honey. One Saturday, Ṭayọ and his friends went to the Liberty Stadium in Ibadan to watch one important international final

football match between I. I. C.C Shooting Stars of Ibadan
and Canon de Yaoundé of Cameroon. Thousands of fans
from all over the country came to watch the match. As Tayọ
and his friends were about to queue to buy their tickets, he
sighted Senior Abẹki. Their eyes met but because the Senior
was hugging one of his girlfriends he came to the stadium
with, Tayọ acted as if he did not see him and his girl. Senior
Abẹki called and said, "Tayọ, come here."

Tayọ left the queue and went to him reluctantly. Abẹki
wanted Tayọ to greet him and his girlfriend with due
respect but instead he asked, "Senior Abẹki, please what can
I do for you? Abẹki brought out his wallet and said, "Take
this money Tayọ, quickly go and buy some refreshments for
me and my beautiful girl, right?"

"Sorry Senior Abẹki, this match is almost starting and my
friends and I are on this long queue to buy our tickets as
you can see. I won't be able to oblige," he said and handed
his money back to him.

Abẹki collected his money with his mouth agape. Tayọ
knew he was slighted but he did not care. He left him and
his girl and went back to the queue. The following Monday
in school, Abẹki came to Tayọ's class. He excused the
teacher who was teaching in the class and said,

"Tayọ, see me unfailingly after the school hours in my class
this afternoon."

Tayọ just nodded. After the school closed for the day, he went to see him. Immediately he entered the class, he greeted,

"Good afternoon Senior Abẹki."

Instead of returning Tayọ's greeting, Abẹki said, "Was it you I and my girlfriend saw last Saturday at the Liberty Stadium?"

"Yes, Senior."

"I told you now," Abẹki said and looked at the other senior that was with him in the class.

"So, it is true that you misbehaved to your senior? You are a stupid boy. You think any local junior student like you can mess your seniors up and go unpunished? We won't take that from any of you. I mean it. And, you'll learn the lesson of your life this beautiful afternoon," the other senior threatened.

"No, Senior, but em....em....please let me expla......."

Before Tayọ could finish his sentence, Abẹki gave him a slap and cross-tackled him. Tayọ fell. Students often called that type of slap in their slang, *igbaju olooyi*[2]. As he tried to quickly run out from the class fearing for his dear life, Abẹki's friend shut the door. He took Tayọ by his shirt collar and gagged his mouth. Both seniors started kicking and slapping him. He became powerless. When he almost gave up the ghost, Abẹki shouted at him, "Be on your knees before I get rid of you. " As Tayọ wanted to obey his command, he fell and passed out. Both seniors opened the classroom door at once and took to their heels leaving Tayọ dying. A student who was outside saw both seniors run out of the class. The student quickly entered the class to check what was pursuing them. He found Tayọ unconscious. He ran straight back outside and shouted for help. Some teachers and students who were still in the school premises rushed into the class. They tried their best to bring Tayọ round but he was too weak to say anything coherent. They carried him to the staff room.

"This is a serious matter. Let's take him to the hospital immediately," one of the teachers said.

Tayọ was taken to the hospital and treated. Investigation into what took place started when he was still in the hospital. Not much was achieved. The student who alerted others about what happened said he did not recognise the two seniors who ran away. The teacher who was teaching when Abẹki came and asked Tayọ to report to him in his class stated his side of the story but Abẹki denied that he was the one who maltreated Tayọ. After a few days in the hospital, he recovered and got discharged. He was interviewed and he revealed how everything happened right from the stadium's incident to the time he was almost murdered in the senior's class.

On the assembly one day, the principal asked Abẹki and his friend to come out. The assembly became quiet. Both sauntered out. The principal told the students all that happened between the two seniors and Tayọ. He thanked the quick-thinking student who rushed into the class and called the attention of the school community to what might have turned out horribly.

He said further, "Apart from what the police have done, I have personally spoken to these two seniors and their parents. We will not allow this school to be turned into a place where students bully one another. This school will not be a place where students are afraid to come and learn or where you are not free. After the case has been thoroughly investigated, we have decided to expel these two offenders and I believe all of you will learn some lessons from this." As he was saying that last bit, pandemonium broke out.

Abẹki told the principal, "You are mad Ọgá[3]. No one can expel any of us. If you try it, you and this school should be awaiting the consequences. You will not know peace. That's for sure."

Abẹki snatched the cane which the principal was holding from him and threw it back into the assembly. His friend kicked a teacher violently. Students were running all about. The two ran towards the locked school gate and jumped over the school fence. The principal and the teachers later went back to the staff room and held an impromptu meeting. They called for another assembly. The police arrived at the school premises and its surrounding areas. The principal after a lengthy speech, told the students to go back to their classes and get on with their normal studies.

"We'll inform you in due course of any further development on this case," he said.

But that day, there was no further information from the school. The following day, the students were told in the assembly that Abẹki and his friend were no more students of Origbo High School.

"The police have arrested them. They are now in their custody under investigation. Their parents are cooperating with the police," the principal said.

The information calmed the nerves of everyone. In the end, Abẹki and his friend were expelled. Both of them were brought back to the school by the police to tender their unreserved apology to the students and staff. The court sent them to a corrective centre to be rehabilitated.

Since that sad event, Tayọ was never himself again. He recoiled in horror each time he remembered that incident. He hardly socialised and he stopped doing well in his studies. This gave his subject teachers and the school some concern. One day, Mr Aliu, his class teacher in Form 1, told him to come and see him during the long break. Tayọ loved him as a teacher as he always remembered how he helped him to fit in properly when he started his high school.

When he went to see him, he asked, "Tayọ, how has your day been?"

"It's been good sir."

"Sure?"

"Yes sir."

"Well, I have been observing you and the reports I get from other teachers about you since that incident happened have not gladdened my heart. I know what happened knocked you down and that is what can happen to anyone in your shoes. But today, I'm here to tell you why you must move past what you experienced. I know you well. You're a very courageous and diligent student. That incident that took place was a sad occurrence but that should not rob you of your future which remains very bright. You're lagging in your studies. You started well but remember, your future starts from every effort you put into your studies from the time you were given admission to this school till the time you'll sit your final exam. You didn't do anything wrong when you were attacked but those who subjected you to such savagery, as you've been told, are now in a corrective centre. If they cooperate with the authority, what they did won't be the end of their lives, they'll just learn from it and move on. Their destiny is still in their hands. So, think about this, if you allow what they did to you to derail your dream and strip you of your future, if they end up achieving greatness in life, Tayọ, who loses? You. And, Tayọ, it's not only when you do something wrong that you suffer. At times, people do suffer for what they don't even know anything about. Do you know and believe that?"

"Em…em…. em well, it may be true sir."

"Good. Can you think of persons you've read about or seen who have suffered for what they never knew anything about?"

"Em…em…em…. I can't think of any for now, sir."

"That's okay. We'll look at good two examples. You once told me that as a Christian when you were growing up, you were made to attend Sunday School classes, is that still true?"

"Still true sir."

"Good. As a former Sunday School student, what can you say about Jesus Christ briefly?"

"We were taught that God, His Father, sent Him to us to save us. He healed the sick, opened the eyes of the blind, raised the dead, fed the poor, loved those that people hated and told the truth all the time."

"Whoa. Tayọ, you were taught all these about Jesus Christ as young as you were then?"

"Yes sir. I still go to church to know more about Jesus and His Father and heaven."

"For all those good things you said Jesus did, was He loved or hated by His people?"

"He was so much hated those Roman rulers nailed Him to the cross to curry favour from their subjects. Till now, I still ask myself why they treated Him that way."

"You are good Tayọ. That's that on Jesus Christ. Have you ever heard or read anything about Nelson Mandela?"

"Yes sir, in our civic subject class in primary school and in our government class when I was offering the subject."

"Can you tell me anything about him?"

"Yes sir. So much. He was from South Africa and a black man like us. We were taught that he told the *Oyinbos*[4] to go back to their country and to stop maltreating his African people. When they refused, South African people formed a political party in 1912 which was supported by all Africans. I can't remember the name of the party but…. em…em…."

"This is interesting. Do you mean the African National Congress (ANC)?"

"Thank you, sir. That was the party."

"And what happened after that?"

"The white people became afraid. They tried everything possible to silence all the ANC leaders."

"Did they succeed?"

"To a certain extent sir. They killed so many Africans who demanded that they must be given freedom in their own

country. They sent many to jail including Nelson Mandela.
He spent 27 years in prison. I hate what the white people did
to the South African people, coming especially after the bitter
experience of the slave trade. And in their own country! It was
pure injustice. I once asked my civic teacher in primary school
why all Africans didn't rise up and fight the white people."

"And what was his response?"

"He told me Africans tried their best but em…. Sir, I wasn't
satisfied with that answer till date. And em…."

"Well, what happened to Mandela after 27 years in prison?"

"He was eventually released by President F. W. de Klerk
because of the growing internal and external pressure and
fears of racial civil war."

"Whoa! Tayọ, you know so much about Mandela!"

"Thank you, sir. Yes. I still love to read about him and all
that happened during the sanctioned racial segregation and
political and economic discrimination against non-whites
in South Africa in newspapers. I watch documentaries
about his heroic life any time I have the opportunity. The
white people didn't do well at all. Just because they were
more powerful, they treated other human beings like
animals. They took over other people's economic means
and punished them severely for saying 'no'. Sir, I don't
understand."

"That's where I am going this afternoon. If Jesus and Mandela were treated that way despite all they tried to do to make sure this world is fair to all of us, can you see that till date, people just detest the truth and hate being disobeyed or asked to act fairly? Mind you, it isn't only the white people that are bad or wicked. As you have bad ones among them so you have among us. We're all human beings. Many times, people suffer and punish other people just for the fun of it."

"You are correct sir. Hum…. em….But on the issue of Jesus, I have observed and I have seen that you are a devoted Muslim. How come you know all these things about Jesus Christ?"

Mr Aliu laughed and said, "Tayọ, that's not an issue. As a human being, you have to know as much as possible about other people's background: their religion, language, food, marriage and other customs. That's how it should be. Knowledge of such things will help you to look at things from different angles. I believe you know some things about Muslims and our religion. Is that right?"

"Yes, you are right sir. Back then in my locality when I was in primary school, many villagers were Muslims and many were Christians. There was no Muslim school in our area at that time, all of us attended Christian missionary schools and we learned together without any problem. We all lived together in peace. We were taught in school how The Prophet Muhammed went on Hijra to escape persecution.

During Christmas, Muslims would visit and celebrate with us and during Salah, we would go and celebrate with them. We did everything communally. We always looked forward to such celebrations unlike now that each religion is being pitched against the other by our political and religious leaders. Then, Christians were not killing Muslims and vice versa."

"Good you understand all that. Back to our discussion. From now, see what happened to you in the hands of those seniors as a punishment you did not deserve. That's why the school, all parents and even the government stood by you so that others may learn lessons that wickedness in whatever form does not pay. That said, Tayọ, can you promise you will be your former self or be better than what you were before the incident happened and face your studies squarely?"

"I promise sir. You have enlightened me so much today. I love to listen to you. I'll take to your advice and make a change."

"Good, clap for yourself."

"Thank you, sir." The mentor and the mentee ended on that note and the meeting brought positive changes to Tayọ's school life which delighted everyone.

～

If you are a teacher, never see yourself as the untouchable. In Tayọ's school there were some expatriate teachers. Some were Ghanaians, Indians, Britons and Germans. One of the English teachers was British. The lady was of average height and moderate in size. She was simply beautiful. Students often talked about her beauty but those were however the positive qualities she possessed. She was tough and wicked. She was a dictator to the core. Some students often ran away from her class giving one excuse or the other. Her mastery of beating students with cane was legendary. Any poor performance in any English class work by students often brought out her raw anger. Mrs Stone, as she was called, fitted her character perfectly well because she was as hard as stone. All students who passed through her class never spoke many positive things about her. To make matters worse, she expected students to mimic her British accent and even behave like the British. When this had gone on for too long, one anonymous student wrote a note and put it in the school's suggestion box one day. In the note was written in capital letters, "MRS HAVES STONE, YOU ARE A DEVIL INCARNATE. PLEASE MR PRINCIPAL, SEND THIS WOMAN BACK TO BRITAIN."

The principal always read out notes from the suggestion box fortnightly without any prior knowledge of the notes' content. Mrs Stone was in the assembly when the principal read the note to everyone. The principal would not have read it if he knew what it contained though as a rule, he was supposed to. The students shouted in support of what the

principal read out. This infuriated all the teachers and the
principal greatly. The principal immediately asked all
Forms 1 and 2 students to march to their classes. After they
had gone, he asked all Forms 3, 4 and 5 students to go on
their knees. He lambasted them for showing a seed of
discord in the school and teaching the junior students the
wrong way to behave. He apologised profusely to Mrs
Haves Stone on behalf of the school. He ordered the
students to say 'sorry' to Mrs Stone but only a few obeyed
his order. The principal was raging with anger for the
students' disobedience. He said all Forms 3, 4 and 5
students should each be given six strokes of the cane. He
assigned two teachers to each class for the task. All the
students took their punishment in good faith having
achieved what their aim was, to disgrace Mrs Stone publicly
for the first time ever. Mrs Stone was dejected. The
principal and other staff members tried in vain to find out
the anonymous writer but they never succeeded. That
incident brought an end to the usage of the school
suggestion box.

One morning long after the incident, Mrs Stone came to
teach English in one class. She was teaching some difficult
words in a comprehension passage. She first asked the
students one by one to read out the passage paragraph by
paragraph. As they were doing that, she was taking note of
words they mispronounced or found difficult to pronounce
on the chalkboard for drilling exercise. When they finished
the reading, she put Jerry Obong on the spot and asked him

to pronounce 'European''. He pronounced it with the main stress on the first syllable instead of the second syllable and also pronounced its initial sound differently. That, as usual, did not go well with Mrs Stone. She asked him to listen carefully to how she pronounced the word two times but Jerry kept pronouncing the same thing. She thought Jerry was unnecessarily being stubborn. She walked to his seat and started hitting his head with the cane in her hand.

She said, "You're stubborn. You're stubborn. You're a stubborn goat."

All other students kept quiet in order not to get into trouble with her again.

"Odoziaku Stone, biko, apiazi namu itali. Ogini kamu mere gi?"[5] Jerry asked in his Igbo native language.

Mrs Stone, who did not understand a word in Igbo Language thought Jerry had used his language to abuse her. In annoyance, she said, "You're very stupid Jerry. Yes, stupid. How dare you talk to me in vernacular. Have you not been warned enough not to speak vernacular in the class? You've abused me and I bet you'll pay for your rudeness. I was appointed to come and teach you, not to come and be embarrassed."

Mrs Stone picked something on the ground and threw it at Jerry. It hit him in the face very close to his right eye. Blood gushed out. All other students rushed out of the classroom in total confusion. Other teachers and students went to the

class to see what was happening. Mrs Stone just stood like a
statue. She did not know what to do. She could not talk. She
was just shaking. Jerry was attended to and taken to the
nearest clinic as it seemed blood was coming out from his
right eye socket. In the ensuing disorder, some senior
students 'arrested' Mrs Stone. They blindfolded her and
dragged her to one of the school's toilets and tied her hands
to her back. They threatened to kill her if Jerry lost any of
his eyes. The whole school environment was turned upside
down. The event snowballed into a riot, the school gates
were barricaded by angry students and some other tough
and unyielding teachers who used to behave to students
badly were attacked as they wanted to bolt. At last, Mrs
Stone, the iron lady, was bent like a fresh fish. She begged
and cried like a baby in the toilet where she was being kept.
Suddenly, police arrived and started firing canisters of tear
gas into the school premises. Students and teachers ran in
all directions leading out of the school. Nobody knew who
called the police. Many sustained injuries and few students
were arrested. Students holding Mrs Stone in captivity ran
away when they felt the effect of the tear gas. The police
later rescued her from the school toilet. She almost lost her
life. Tayọ had never seen a situation where a British person
in Nigeria was dealt with like that before. He believed it was
a taboo to retaliate even when Britons maltreat you. But
after all, seeing is believing. The principal, when he came
out from his hiding, closed the school down indefinitely.

The government waded into the crisis and set up a committee to investigate the remote and immediate causes of the sordid incident. Students that were arrested were released. Before the school was reopened, Mrs Stone was reprimanded for causing bodily harm to one of her students and she was asked to pay for Jerry's hospital treatment. Jerry was asked to write an apology letter to her and all students were compelled to pay damages for the school property they vandalised. They were told for the umpteenth time never to speak vernacular in the class. Few months later, Mrs Stone got herself transferred to another school. Teachers became more cautious and friendly to their students. What happened that day seemed to have done something good at least - students who were used to being treated like animals by some teachers enjoyed some respite.

CHAPTER TEN

P eople are often unreasonable, irrational, and self-
centred, forgive them anyway - Mother Teresa

Dupẹ was undergoing training at Oluyoro
Catholic Hospital, Ibadan to become a nurse assistant. She
narrated her life journey to her boss at work when they
were having a chat one day. From then, Dupẹ's boss
developed interest in her. She asked her if she could live
with her and her family for a few years so she could save
some money and further her education. She moved in with
her and every weekend, she allowed her to attend evening
lessons in her preparation to sit GCE examination. Her boss
encouraged her that it was possible for her to pass the exam
if she worked hard. With that assurance, she worked and
studied very hard hoping that one day, she too might
become a professional nurse.

During one of his holidays in Form 3, Tayọ and Dupẹ visited Uncle Ezekiel and his family. By that time, Ikẹ had got admission into the university to study pharmacy. Her uncle had retired but he kept himself occupied doing some business. They were delighted to see Dupẹ and Tayọ. They talked on so many issues concerning their family.

"You are both very welcome," their uncle and his wife said.

"Thank you very much. We didn't even know Ikẹ would be at home when we planned to visit."

"I'm very glad to see both of you after such a long time. How are you doing generally? Do you still go to see our grandmother?" Ikẹ asked.

"Yes. Grandmother is doing well in the village. She missed all of us so much. She's just such a lovely old woman," Dupẹ said.

"Dupẹ, when have you last seen or heard anything from your mother?" Ezekiel asked.

"It's quite a long time. I went to say hello to our grandmother some months back. I asked her if she had heard any news from our mother, and she said she did at times".

"During the next holiday, is it possible for three of us to go and see our mother to know how she's doing? Since she's refused to change, could we at least go and find out what her problems are?" Ikẹ suggested.

"Well, I think we can go if everything works out well. Our grandmother will be very happy to hear this," Dupẹ said.

"I support that. You can all go and see things for yourself," Ezekiel added.

"I will not go with you," Tayọ, who had kept quiet all along once their talk shifted to that issue, told them bluntly.

"Why won't you like to go and see your mother?" Ezekiel asked.

"Uncle, I don't really just want to go sir. I think meeting her can make me very sad. I don't know if you understand what I'm talking about. That's the way I always feel each time I think about our mother."

"But are you the only one she ran away from? Don't be stubborn. You should know you've got to forgive and forget," Ikẹ said philosophically.

"Forgive and forget? That's hard. But I'm not saying that can't happen in future. For now, I still carry the huge wound of her not being there when we needed her most. Both of you are free to go, sorry, count me out," he said.

"I can understand where you're coming from and I feel especially for you, your sisters and your grandmother. It can be hard and painful as you have said. That's all right if you don't want to go with them. Dupẹ and Ikẹ, try to understand. The two of you can go. What about that?"

"Thank you, uncle. I really appreciate you. You always understand my position on many issues when others seem not to. Thank you, sir," Tayọ said before his sisters could say anything further.

"I appreciate that coming from you Tayọ, but you should understand this. Some people will misinterpret you because of so many factors that are beyond their comprehension most times. Your father told me your mother came to see him one day, but I did not probe further what happened during that visit between them."

"Tayọ, did our father tell you that our mother visited him?" Dupẹ asked.

"I don't think he told me." He said though he remembered his father told him that his mother paid him a visit one day.

"That's okay. I'm happy you said there's room for forgiveness later in life. That's quite possible and I pray such a time will come sooner than later," their uncle said.

"Amen," Dupẹ and Ikẹ said.

Uncle Ezekiel and his family made them feel at home. For the few days during their stay, they visited many places of interest that made their journey an unforgettable experience. When they were about to leave, Ikẹ, Ezekiel and his wife appealed to Tayọ and Dupẹ to focus on their studies, as people say, the end justifies the means.

"You know God works in miraculous ways. At present, Dupẹ is training to become a nursing assistant and she is at the same time, studying to sit her GCE exam. Later, she will train to become a qualified nurse. Before she started primary school some years ago, almost everybody had written her off as one of those young women that would be married off without any career. Fast forward her case, in few years' time, we will all be calling her, 'Nurse Dupẹ'. Won't that be wonderful? That's why the Bible says, 'Man proposes, God disposes'.[1] Please, all of you should face your future with great hope and fortitude. I hope your experience will be a positive lesson for many others in the world who may think there's no way to flourish after some setbacks," their uncle appealed to them.

"Thank you, uncle. You're always there for us and your encouragement and usual assistance have seen us this far. We pray God will continue to bless you. We are so grateful," Dupẹ said.

"It can only be God, my daughter. What I have gone through in life has taught me that there's no mountain that human beings cannot climb with determination. I should thank you all for being very assiduous young people. God bless you richly."

Ikẹ told Dupẹ and Tayọ that when she finished her course in pharmacy in the university, she might come to Ibadan to work as a pharmacist at the University College Hospital, (UCH).

"If our uncle allows you, why not? We will be happy to see you in Ibadan. You can't compare our city to anywhere else. It's a very peaceful and lovely city to live in. I love to live in Ibadan I must confess," Tayọ said.

"I think most people would agree with you on that Tayọ," Ezekiel's wife said.

When Dupe and Tayọ were leaving, their uncle gave them some money and presents. Dupẹ promised to come back for another visit anytime she was free to do so.

Dupẹ and Ikẹ paid their mother a visit as planned. When they got to her village, she was not around. They were told she and her husband had gone to the farm early that morning. The two went from one house to the other to greet the villagers. The villagers still remembered Dupẹ who had come there once. Their stepfather came back first from the farm and told them their mother would soon come back. He was very pleased to see them after such a long time. As they were still talking, their mother came. She did not hide her displeasure at seeing them.

"Welcome Mama, we have been here for a few hours waiting for you to come back from the farm. Hope you are ok."

"Ah. Dupẹ, Ikẹ welcome. But you should both be at work by now. Why are you here today?"

"We are here because we want to see you after such a long time."

"Thank you for that. When are you going back?" their mother asked without bothering to ask what they would like to eat.

"But I've been telling you this. Are these not your children? Is this how to behave to your own children? When will you change this attitude? Won't you ask them what they will eat? Can't you be cheerful and be polite to your own children and make them feel at home? Indeed, your own type of a mother is as scarce as a virgin in a maternity ward. Haba! Who did this to you?" her husband who was watching and listening to their discussion spoke out in annoyance.

"How has an issue between a mother and her children become your own problem Mr Busybody? Does that concern you? They are my children and my behaviour to them should not be your own cup of tea. Do you hear that?"

"Mama, your behaviour isn't good if I have to tell you the truth, if not for today but for your own future, please change. Remember, there's always a payback day. What he said is what any other reasonable person would have said. Can we blame Tayọ for deciding not to come with us to see you? If we too...."

"Stop there, you are not serious. Don't talk to me like that. I am your mother. And who is that disrespectful small boy you are talking about? Do I really care what becomes of him? Since I have been on my own, have I asked any of you to come and see me? If any of you likes, you can come. If you don't like, don't come to see me. So, do you expect me to make a feast to welcome you?"

"When you are not insane this woman, why do you always put your foot in your mouth? Your behaviour and utterances will soon bring you problems. You know I tell you this all the time," her husband said matter-of-factly.

Ikẹ was furious. Both of them stood up to go back home at that point. They felt nauseously sad thinking how any mother would behave like that to her children.

"Mama, your behaviour is beyond ordinary. I think something is wrong. Mama, look at it this way. This life is too short to decide to go through it the way you are doing things. We appeal to you to change, it's not too late," Dupẹ said. They were happy that their brother, Tayọ wasn't with them. If he was, no one would have been able to persuade him not to leave at once.

"*Hum.... hum....There are mothers and there are mothers,*" her husband said to himself.

Amidst tears, Dupẹ said, "Thank you. We are going. If this is the best way you should behave to us as our mother, it's between you and your conscience."

Though they had spent all their money on transport, they decided not to ask their mother for any money. As they were about to move outside from the house, their stepfather called and appealed to them not to go back that day. They told him they had to leave. Before they left, he said, 'If you are not living witnesses to what happened today, you may be thinking I've been responsible for your mother's sordid misbehaviour to all of you including her own mother. Her case is unique. There are many women who, due to one problem or the other, have left their husbands, even in this village. Still, they continue to shower love on their children. No one, I'm sure, understands your mother's problem but herself. Thank goodness, you are here to see it yourselves."

As her husband was saying that, Ọmọyẹ looked embarrassed and sober. Both children shook their heads in disbelief. She went to them and said almost crying, "Dupẹ and Ikẹ, my daughters, sorry, I didn't mean to hurt you. You are lovely children. Don't be angry with me. I do things I later regret. I'll try and change as you've advised. At times, I can't help myself."

After she appealed to them not to be annoyed with her, she gave the two of them two gallons of palm oil and a basket of *garri*. "Tell Tayọ to also find time to come and see me. Don't mind what I had said earlier on about him. And Ikẹ, how is Ezekiel and his family doing? Is it well with all of them?"

"Yes, they are all doing well."

Their mother and her husband saw them off to the lorry station but when the lorry they were going with arrived, their mother held on to both of them for few minutes and cried. Ikẹ and Dupẹ also cried. Their mother's unpredictable behaviour to them was a serious concern to the girls. When they got back, both related their bitter experience to their uncle.

"One thing I would like you to know is this," he began, "your mother must have probably had some problem when she was growing up. That must have toughened her from the beginning. Her parents might not have noticed this but I'm sure there are some secrets behind what she's doing. That problem developed into a habit which she has found very difficult to do away with. You should all take her as she is. At present, there's nothing much you can do to change her. You said she later apologised and cried, that's reassuring. We'll all need to intercede for her in prayer believing there's no one that God can't change. God might lead her to tell us one day what's behind her strange behaviour. You don't need to tell Tayọ everything that happened. He may find it very difficult to accept your mother as she is." Though Ezekiel knew it was bad for her to have behaved like that, *nobody counts fingers of a six-fingered person in their presence.*[2] Dupẹ saw Tayọ the following week. She told him that their mother asked of him and even sent an invitation to him to come and visit her in the village.

"Why did you tell her you saw me in the first instance?" Tayọ asked, his eyes becoming red.

"So, you think I wouldn't tell her about you when she asked of you?"

"Next time, please, tell her you don't know my whereabouts if you don't want trouble. I hope you get that clear."

"No problem, but that's bad of you. Do you think you have two mothers? Better accept her as your mother as we do, though we know it's hard. And, two wrongs don't make a right," Dupé said. She was afraid Tayọ's rigid attitude towards their mum might negatively affect him in future.

"Does that concern you? Or have I asked you to tell me who my mother is? Please, I've got my own life to live. Mind your own business. There are many people who do not have mothers that are better off, don't you know that?" he asked on his way out from the room.

"All the best for you then," Dupẹ shot him a look and closed the door.

CHAPTER ELEVEN

Every day is for the thief, one day is for the owner - Nigerian adage

Form 4D was an art class and it was noted for serious behaviour problems. It was made up of twenty-two boys and eight girls. It was in that class that students could be found with cigarettes, Chinese Capsule (CC) or wine bottles. Fighting because of sarcastic comments was the order of the day. Ironically, many of the students were very brilliant. They always brought honour to the school especially in sports. Though they were always punished for offences they committed, their notoriety was a source of concern to the school authorities. Any serious offence perpetrated in or out of the school environment was often attributed to Form 4D students until it could be proved otherwise. As a result, they were often punished for the offence they might not even know anything about. At times the school would offer a belated apology to Form 4D students for punishing them wrongly. The school used corporal and face-the-sun punishment, portion cutting, suspension and dismissal as weapons but those methods failed to solve the whole problem.

The school once decided to move the class closer to the office of their no-nonsense principal. In the assembly one morning, the principal announced,

"During our last staff meeting, this school has decided to move Form 4D class to Form 2C class from this morning. Yes, you've all heard me well; from this morning. We're doing this for two reasons. one, to de-escalate Form 4 D students' violent behaviour as much as possible. Two, this will give me a personal chance to monitor their unruly behaviour. When this assembly ends in few minutes' time, Form 2C students, go back to your class, take all your belongings out from there and go straight to Form 4D. All students in Form 4D should do the same simultaneously. I'm giving you 30 minutes to carry out this task.

"In addition, I have been briefed by the Government studies teacher for Form 4D that all of you are taking the subject. On Wednesday every fortnight starting from next week, I will be taking your Government class between 1pm and 2pm, that's immediately after your long break. If you love yourself dearly, neither come late to my class nor be absent. If you want to be absent at all, mark my words, you must get a note from your parents for me, a week before the class holds. Form 4D students, do you understand everything I've said so far?"

"Yes sir," they all said.

The principal was always the final arbiter in any serious case involving students with the school staff and outsiders. All students called him *Baba fọka.*[1] He was always ruthless when it came to beating stubborn students. The most horrible part of his method of discipline was that almost all parents supported his way of dealing with his students and they always thanked him for his no-nonsense attitude during any PTA meetings in the presence of students. So, if he beat any student, such a student needed not report to his/her parents because doing that would bring more trouble. Any student's case getting to the principal's attention in the first place was an inexcusable offense most parents would not condone.

"Now, Form 2C and Form 4D students, will you march to your class and carry out my instruction right away."

"Yes sir," they all said. All the staff nodded in agreement while many Form 4D students put their hands on their heads thinking of what those drastic actions would mean for them.

During an English lesson after that shake-up, a boy stole another student's Practical English textbook. An elderly and a well-respected English teacher came into Class 4D that morning. The students nicknamed the teacher Baba Ponpo.

The name was coined from his real name by the students. The previous day, he had warned that those students without Practical English textbooks should not bother to come to his class. He was a man of his words.

"Good morning students," he began. "If you are here without your Practical English textbook, stand up." Some students stood up immediately.

"Move out here please."

They all moved out but one of the students, Bisi, a girl, was panting. She looked inside her locker and bags, under the chairs and her surroundings, she could not find her Practical English textbook which she had used in the morning to do her assignment.

"Please class, who took my English textbook?" she asked almost crying but nobody responded. The teacher beat those that did not have their textbooks.

Then he said, "You," pointing to Bisi, "come out here for your punishment."

"But em…. em…. No sir, I came to school with my textbook this morning. It was from it I completed my assignment. I'm sure of that sir."

"Are you sure you are telling the truth?" the teacher asked and looked worried as he knew the type of students he was dealing with in that class.

"Definitely yes, sir."

"Could you all check that you are not with her English textbook? Look inside your lockers and bags, you might have probably taken her book by mistake. Also, check the names on your own copy." They all checked but the book could not be found.

"Since her textbook is missing and she was sure she brought it to school, I suspect one of you has stolen that book. I suspect too, that the person might have taken it out to be kept with someone outside this class in order that she might be punished. Last week, it was money, today, it is a textbook. Tomorrow, who knows what next? One day, God will expose the thieves. Once again, check your individual lockers and bags," he directed. When the second round of checking had been completed, the teacher was looking defeated but he did not give up.

He said, "All stand." All the students stood up. "Don't touch anything from now. Don't bend down. Remain standing. I have the feeling that her textbook is still in this class. Class captain, assistant captain and Bisi, come out here." Fear was written on the students' faces and the class became silent.

"I will be looking at every one of your mates while the three of you will carry out another check. Look inside the lockers and bags one by one, check line by line and person by person. Check the name on each textbook. There is no glory in training students who will become tomorrow's notorious criminals. Their stealing activity must be nipped in the bud day by day," he said.

They started to check everyone and everywhere line by line. The teacher stood at the only entrance to the class. He kept a close watch on each student. A biology teacher who was going to the next class greeted him. As he turned to exchange greetings with her, one of the boys, Innocent Agbaka, who sat on the last seat of the first row in the class quickly took out the English textbook from his bag and threw it onto another boy's locker next to him. In order not to be falsely accused of stealing the book, the boy shouted, "See, see, everybody see. Innocent, you're a thief. You threw this book on my table just now, yes, you did." He held the book tightly and pointed it in Innocent's direction.

"Who threw that book?" the teacher asked laughing

"It was Innocent sir," the boy shouted.

"You are crazy. Are you accusing me of stealing the book?" Innocent boldly asked.

"You threw it. You threw it. Don't tell lies." Many other students who saw him throw the book spoke at once. Both Innocent and the boy were called out. Innocent, the accused, became very nervous.

"Okay, who among you saw him when he threw the book?" the teacher directed the question to those who were sitting near the two boys.

"It was Innocent sir," Aina, Tade and Ṣọla unanimously said.

"Innocent is a thief," Grace, who was Innocent's sworn enemy, started to sing.

"Thief," other students chorused.

"Another student's money."

"Thief."

"Another student's book!"

"Thief."

Innocent who began to shake like a leaf shot the girl a look and said, "If I catch you, I will deal with you. Better know that."

"God catches you today," Grace continued while the English teacher behaved as if he didn't hear them sing.

"Thief."

"Everybody, come and see the face of tomorrow's armed robber."

"Thief."

"God catches you today."

"Thief."

"Silence," the English teacher said. "I must not hear any word again from any of you. Class captain, come, stand here and write names of stubborn students who might still say something after I have left this class." As he said that, he asked Innocent to follow him to the staff room.

"Why did you steal that book?" the teacher asked Innocent on their way to the staff room.

"Pardon me sir. Please don't take me to the staff room sir," Innocent pleaded.

"I can pardon you, but only if you tell me the truth. Why did you steal that book in the first instance? Can you tell me why, Innocent?"

"Sir, I was not interested in stealing her textbook. When she was doing some exercise from it this morning, I saw some money inside the book. I took the book hoping I would get a chance to take the money and return her book but em….em….em….I know now that what I did was wrong."

"Do you think the money is still there?"

"I think so sir," the teacher opened the book and truly, he found some money inside.

"Go back to the class and tell Bisi to report to me immediately." Innocent went and came back with Bisi who looked very worried.

"Bisi, where did you get these new currency notes you put in your English textbook?

"I was given sir."

"Who gave you, your father or your mother?"

"No sir."

"Who gave you the money?"

Bisi knelt down and started begging, "Please sir, it's, it's em…. Please sir, it's…."

"Okay, for the last time Bisi, from where did you get this money? If you fail to tell me now, I'm inviting your parents to this school tomorrow so we can get to the root of where the money came from. Okay?"

"No sir. Don't invite them. I will tell you. "

"I'm listening."

"My man…. em…. em…. man…. friend gave me the money sir."

"You mean you have a sugar daddy?"

"Yeeees sir. No sir."

"You have a manfriend, you, Bisi?" the teacher asked again.

"No sir…. em….em….Yes sir. Sorry sir."

"Okay Innocent, go back to your class. I will be dealing with your case tomorrow."

"Thank you, sir."

"One point before you go. Make sure no one else hears what you have just witnessed. If that happens and you're found to be the storyteller, that'll be another serious case for you. Hope that's understood?"

"Yes sir. I promise sir." Innocent left with the promise to keep what happened to himself.

Back to you Bisi, "What's the name of your sugar daddy? Where does he live? What does he do for a living? Since when has he been giving you money? How much did he give you the last time? Do your parents give you money or not? Do some of your friends have sugar daddies too?" the teacher who was angry kept on asking her questions.

"No but.... but.... but...."

"But what?"

"Yes sir. Em.... em...."

"All these questions need answers. Bisi, go home and think about them. Once you arrive at school tomorrow morning, come straight here to see me. Have I made myself understood?"

"Hum.... Please.... sir....Yes sir. I'm in trouble," she said as she was about to go.

"Before you go, let's count how much is in your textbook. This is your book. Open it and count the money yourself."

Bisi counted and said, "100-naira, sir."

The teacher counter-checked and said, "This is a pen. Write the amount here on this piece of paper and sign it."

Bisi did as she was directed.

"You can go. I'll see you tomorrow."

The following morning, Innocent went to see the teacher to find out what his punishment would be for his attempt to steal money and make another student suffer.

"Innocent, when I asked in the class for two consecutive times for the book to be returned, why didn't you own up and return it?"

"Sorry sir. I was about to…. But…I….em….was afraid….em….I…."

"But because of the money you wanted to steal, you refused to take responsibility for your action. What a shame. You are a thief and you've been found out," the teacher told Innocent who was about to cry.

The principal and other school teaching staff deliberated on what to do with his case. During the assembly that afternoon, the principal said,

"We have been ringing this into your ears, all of you, that stealing for whatever reason or in whatever form is bad. Nobody is Mr Have-it-All. But one must be contented with whatever one has. Innocent has brought shame onto himself and his parents. All the thieves in this school will be caught one by one. If you're one of them, stop stealing. And for many of you that are honest and hardworking, keep these up. Those are best two qualities you could ever covet.

Your parents might be poor, but they still work very hard to
make sure you're educated. How come some of you want
the easy way out? This is a warning and a great lesson for all
of you. Innocent, remove your shirt. Lie down. Give me
your bare back. Don't move. No shaking. If you do, I will
start your punishment all over," the principal with one
strong cane in his hand ordered.

Innocent looked at the cane and the principal fearfully and
took to his heels. Some students ran after him and threw
some objects his way. He fell and got wounded. He was
brought back to the principal. He looked remorseful and
willingly obeyed the principal's orders. He gave him six
strokes of the cane. He cried bitterly but he never moved an
inch because he knew the principal would start his
punishment all over as he had vowed. Some few students,
especially boys, felt pity for him. After the beating, the
principal instructed him to come with his parents to the
school the next day.

His parents came and the principal told them, "This school
has decided not to suspend Innocent this being the first
time he has done something silly and shameful like this. But
if this is repeated, the school will not hesitate to suspend or
expel him. Innocent, hope you hear this well."

"Yes sir. Very clear sir," he said. He promised he would never
do something like that again. His parents thanked the
school for giving their son another opportunity. Thus,
Innocent's case was resolved.

That day however, Bisi did not come to school. The following day the school sent a school clerk to her parents to find out why their ward was not in school and to ask them to come to school for an important meeting based on what their daughter did. Bisi, who knew the clerk well and saw him coming to their house quickly fled before her parents knew what was happening. When the clerk came in and delivered the school's message, they asked the clerk to sit down so as to find out from Bisi what happened in school the previous day as she did not tell them anything.

"Bisi, Bisi, Bisi," her father called out loudly. "Are you deaf. Bisi, can't you answer me? If I come to your room, you will find yourself to blame." There was no response from her.

"*Iya* Bisi[2], go and tell your daughter to come here now," Bisi's father ordered.

"Bisi, Bisi, don't you have ears?" her mother was calling as she was going to her room because they were sure she was in the house. She checked her room, but she was not there. She went back to her husband and told him Bisi was not in her room. He did not believe her. Both of them went there and later checked their kitchen, toilet and backyard looking for her. Still, she was nowhere to be found. They became worried.

"Ha-ha, so Bisi. you can do this?" her mother said.

"Ok, Mr School Clerk, we will go with you to your school right away to hear what she has done wrong. It must be a serious matter for her to have bolted. Is it right for us to come with you?"

"I think that should be fine. I don't even know what she has done."

They got to school and the principal welcomed both of them. He sent for the English teacher to come and tell Bisi's parents what happened. He told them everything and showed them the 100-naira notes she claimed her sugar daddy gave her and her signed paper.

"This is unbelievable. We never suspected anything like this was going on. Is it that we have been too careless with our own daughter?" her father asked.

"Don't blame yourself. It can happen to anyone of us. These children are full of doing things that no one could have ever imagined during our own time. But we will get to the root of this matter," the teacher said.

They promised the principal that they would produce their daughter in school to come and answer questions that had been put across to her. They got back home and Bisi was still not in.

"What's the next thing we can do now? I think we have to go out and see if her friends would know her whereabouts," her mother suggested. Their frantic search paid off. She was found in her friend's house. She was brought back home and was asked to confirm what they were told in her school by the principal and her English teacher. She did not deny the allegation.

"Bisi, so it's true! So, you, at this age, have a sugar daddy? *Mo gbe.*"[3] her father lamented. Her mother just stood with her two hands on her head. She was sorry for herself and her family.

"Who must hear this, Bisi? This western education has really brought a lot of problems with it. Sexual immorality, disco dancing, hair jerry-curling, lipstick mouth, clothes that reveal woman's body, high-heel shoes. Love of money. I even saw one of them smoking cigarette one day. Our children cannot speak our own Yorùbá Language which we all understand. I ask, why should some foreign people or any foreign government make a law that our children should not speak our language in our own country and culture and we agreed? *Eleyii ni imunilẹru ẹẹkeji.*[4] No more respect for our culture. Bleaching. Pills and condoms are being sold to kill unborn children and prevent pregnancy. I'm short of words. Everything evil abounds now. All these are abomination and desecration of our valued traditions. *Gbogbo wa ni ironu imunisin nbaja*[5]. Hum…I know it! *Wahala pọnbele ti wọlu*[6]! Bisi, you are a disgrace to our culture, our society and our family. Who taught you this rubbish? *Mo ku!*[7] I know. Yes, I know. You cannot command your own daughters not to go to disco dancing where the boys will be touching them anyhow and anywhere. Um…. These western people came to destroy us and what we stand for. I have seen what others don't probably see. There are bigger problems coming ahead of us. We will see very soon the effects of this western education," Bisi's mother lamented almost crying. To her, Biṣi, her daughter, had gone astray because of so much rubbish she had learnt in school.

"Keep quiet Mama Bisi. Please, do keep quiet now. I don't want to listen to your litany of woes and nonsense again. Stop it now. And, don't blame any western education. Yes, don't blame the western education. Think reasonably, all right? It is this our child, our daughter, Bisi, and her sugar daddy that have gone crazy. Yes, they have gone crazy. *Aye yi ti bajẹ.*[8] But I promise you, we will get to the bottom of this arrant nonsense," he said.

"Ok, no problem, I will keep quiet even though all I'm saying is the fact. We deny them at our own peril. Men, you'll never learn or listen once it's women talking. To most of you, you think women don't have sense. You'll soon see. Better wake up all of you." she replied her husband.

Biṣi's father first wanted to kick his daughter, but he refrained from doing that. He asked her to sit down as she had started sobbing and pleading for mercy.

"Tell us, who is this sugar daddy, where does he live? Is he married? How many wives does he have? What does he do for a living? Did he really give you that large amount of money? And for what? Since when have you been going out with him? Have we not been trying our best to make sure you are not wayward? *Ẹ jọọ ẹyin eniyan, ẹ gba mi.*[9] What is this life turning into? Our forefathers will be crying in their grave. Bisi, please talk or I will...." her father threatened.

Bisi, who did not know which of the questions she could answer said, "I'm sorry Baba. I'm sorry. It was a mistake. I'm sorry. Mama, help me tell Baba that I'm sorry. I beg you. It was a mistake."

"Bisi, Bisi, you're a bad girl!" her mother said.

"Is something wrong with your head? Is 'I'm sorry' your only answer to all my questions?" her father asked as he gave her a slap.

"I'm sorry. Baba, I'm sorry. Yes. But now, I will talk Baba. I'm dead. I don't know, but I can take you to his house. Yes, I know his house. Sorry Baba, I will take you there. Oh, why did I do this?"

"We're going right there now. Mama Bisi, let's go." The two of them in company with Bisi left for the man's house. But the offender had got wind of what happened from one of Bisi's friends who knew about their clandestine relationship.

Her sugar daddy was married with two wives. Being a building contractor, he was very rich. He was also an important community leader, he belonged to the same community association with Bisi's father. Many of his children were older than Bisi. In fact, her father at times would send their community messages of events to the Chief through her. Chief Ojo jocularly often called Bisi 'My daughter'. When they were on Chief Ojo's street, Bisi's father's heart was jumping up and down like somebody running a marathon. He was thinking if it could be true that one of his close friends could be his daughter's sugar daddy. Some few houses to the Chief's residence, Bisi pointed to the house and said, *"Baba*, I'm sorry, Chief Ojo, your friend, forced me into this shameful act. I told him, I told him. I didn't want to do this but he…. he…." She didn't finish the sentence before her father collapsed and passed out. People who had gathered to see what was going on and his wife came to his rescue. Bisi, once again, ran away from the scene of shame she had caused.

Bisi's father was rushed to the hospital. Few days after he got back home, the police who had already arrested Bisi on the instruction of Chief Ojo for defamation of character came to his house to interview him. They also took statements from Bisi's mother, her school principal, the English teacher, and Innocent. The case became acrimonious. Chief Ojo boasted that he would make sure he sent Bisi's entire family to prison for their attempt to incriminate him in a case he never knew anything about. With his political and financial influence, he tried to buy justice. The police, after thorough investigation, charged Chief Ojo to court. He was found guilty of perverting justice and having sexual intercourse with a minor. He was sentenced to two years and asked to pay the hospital bill for Bisi's father's treatment. He was also asked to pay the case legal cost. Bisi was referred to a counsellor. After her counselling session came to an end, she was transferred to another high school where she finished her education. Many of her mates learned serious lessons from her experience.

Initially, Tayọ did not believe Innocent stole the English textbook until he confessed to the crime. The incident brought to his memory an allegation of stealing once levied against him when he was working for Mrs Aka.

Early one Saturday morning after prayers, Tayọ had rushed over his usual house chores. He finished quickly and joined Mrs Aka and her children in her room. At times when Mrs Aka was going nowhere early in the morning, the children would gather in her room and tell stories of all that had happened during that week or months or years past. This could involve satirical comments on any member of the family including Tayọ's unpolished spoken English. They often laughed till tears would be running down their cheek. As Tayọ was not that busy that morning, he was given the privilege to be in the room with the family. Though he dared not make jest of anyone, he could still listen and laugh. After jawing for about an hour, Mrs Aka went into the kitchen and all of them joined her instantly. Preparation for lunch started fully.

"Tayọ, go and bring for me the napkin on the table inside my room," Mrs Aka said.

He quickly left for her room to take the serviette. Unfortunately, the napkin was not on the table. He looked around for it for a few minutes and found it under the bed. He brought it for her and he was asked why it took that long to return. He explained it was not on the table as she had thought.

Ranti, Mrs Aka's daughter, went into their mum's room to have some rest. Immediately she entered the room, she shouted, "Oh, who has stolen my money? This is not the first time. Today the real thief must be known. I left the money beside my pillowcase when we were all in this room and it's now gone. I saw it before we moved to the kitchen. I won't take this lightly."

"Ranti, check my room well and find your money. I don't think anyone could have taken your money."

"No, Mummy, I've checked and it's not here. I know someone has taken my money," she alleged.

All eyes were focussed on Tayọ who was sent into the room some minutes prior to when Ranti went back there. He was greatly embarrassed and dumbfounded.

"Tayọ, you better produce the money where you hid it or I will deal with you now," Ranti threatened him.

Softly and with his two hands on his head, he said, "Sorry sister Ranti, I didn't see any money when I went into Mummy's room not to talk of taking or hiding it anywhere."

"You are a bad boy for denying seeing the money," she said emphatically.

He started to cry.

"Crying will not help you. If you don't bring out my money now, I will beat you."

"You dare not touch that boy. If you have any respect for me, you should have allowed all of us to help you look for the money instead of just shouting at the boy as if you were in a marketplace. Has he ever stolen any money since he's been living with us? Stop your baseless accusation now or…." Mrs Aka angrily lashed out at Ranti. Tayọ got some respite after that comment.

"But Tayọ, if you are the one who took the money," Mrs Aka continued, "stealing is not good. It disgraces and humiliates people. Just tell us. No one will kill you."

Tayọ who knew that he had not taken any money said, "Mummy, I didn't take any money. You can search me and see if I've got any money on me."

"If not for Mummy, you would have known today that stealing is bad. I don't know why mum will always trust people," Ranti said in annoyance and left the kitchen. She went straight to the room and laid in her bed.

Mrs Aka who trusted Tayọ could not have taken the money asked her children to search the room for the money and said, "We can't trust Ranti; she can forget herself. She might have taken the money and kept it somewhere." They started the search and luckily for Tayọ, Ranti found the money inside the pillowcase she was still holding.

She said softly, "No way, my money is here!" She covered her face with the pillowcase.

Mrs Aka laughed sarcastically when she was told that she had found her money. Ranti felt ashamed that she had wrongly accused Tayọ of stealing. She called him into the room and said sorry. Without saying anything, he left the room; he was happy that his name had been cleared.

"Ranti, you can see now, false accusation can be dangerous. If you had checked well, you wouldn't have caused Tayọ this agony. Can you say 'sorry' to him?" her mother commanded.

"Have I not said 'sorry' to you Tayọ? But, 'sorry' again," Ranti said.

"That's okay. Tayọ, sorry for that," Mrs Aka calmed him.

Since that day, Tayọ was always careful not to call somebody a thief unless he was doubly sure he saw that person steal something. He believed that somebody might have dropped the English textbook inside Innocent's locker until he was proved wrong by Innocent's admission of an attempt to steal the money, not the textbook.

CHAPTER TWELVE

I *t is from the black pot that white pap comes* - Nigerian
proverb

Chief Ọbaniyi Awoniyi and his party fulfilled their
political promises. Throughout the five years in power,
their party's Four Cardinal Programmes: Free education
from nursery to tertiary level; free health services;
integrated rural and community development and full and
sustainable employment were followed to the letter. They
surpassed expectations of the masses and opponents. The
western region became a place that citizens were proud of.
They did what past governments had thought was an
impracticability. Before then, poor parents managed to send
their wards just to primary school. With the egalitarian
government in power, they were able to send them to high
school and even university. Parents were only required to
provide their children with feeding and accommodation

and some other luxuries. The government provided for all other things.

However, the general election which was held after the first five years of the civilian rule was rancorous. The ruling party at the centre, The National People's Party of Nigeria (NPPN) was a party of the moneybags and oppressors. They were reactionary in nature. They believed the country and its wealth were for the few rich and their cronies. Their party was for the people only in name as they had a vested interest in maintaining the status quo. To hold firmly to the political and the economic powers at the national and state levels, the NPPN unleashed mayhem before, during and after the elections. They believed the children of the poor being educated by the western regional party would challenge them one day and compete with their own children and thus free the country from the unfairness in governance. They also regarded the progressive, inclusive, outward-looking idea of the UNP as madness. They rigged the elections, killed party opponents and appointed electoral officers who would do their biddings in almost all the electoral districts. They hurriedly appointed judges who would rule in their favour in election disputes in courts. They did everything to remain in power and hijack political authorities in those regions that their party was not controlling. That was because they knew there was no way they would have got votes from the peasants who were enjoying, for the first time, what the political and economic lords in the country had taken away from them for ages.

They did not promise anything tangible to the people in their election manifesto. At the end of the day, almost all the elections at the federal, state and council levels were religiously rigged. Opponents who challenged the polling robbery won nothing at the electoral courts. Citizens believed their actions as a political party were highly irresponsible and reckless.

The country became ungovernable as masses, students included, took to the streets to vent their anger on the political armed robbers. Demonstrators were shot at point-blank range by the government national police. The security agents serving the government in power used Gestapo tactics to crush demonstrators. The government party officials wrote results before votes were counted and declared they had won the elections. They were sworn in by their corrupt judges. All the atrocities were carried out under the aegis of the federal government. That era marked the end of the free and compulsory education in the region.

The country's highly politicised and tribalized jack-booted military came to govern once again on the excuse that the politicians could not govern the country properly. Almost all the indefatigable governors in the LOOBO states that did what the party at the centre thought was incredible were jailed by the military. They suspended the country's constitution and ruled by decrees. Tayọ and thousands of other students who were lucky to have enjoyed free and compulsory education for good five years always thought of the impending difficulty the poor would have to face again due to changes that were certain to take the country backwards.

xxx

Tayọ often moved from one of his friends' houses to another to hide his living condition in his family house during his high school days. For this, he was nicknamed 'roving Tayọ' by some of his mates but his few close friends understood better what he was going through and they never used that against him. He was always eager for the day he would get an admission into a university of his choice and leave for the university campus. He remembered William Shakespeare in *The Merchant of Venice* who said 'All *that glitters isn't gold'* whenever he felt perturbed about the poor state of where he was living. He agreed with the playwright on that because, academically, he was head and shoulders above many of his *ajẹbọta* friends who lived in beautiful houses and had everything going right for them. In fact, it was his cleverness that forced many of them to become his friends. As a result of his accommodation problem, he always left school very late if he was not going to any of his friends' homes. He used his late time in school to do his assignments, play football and help some of his mates with their schoolwork. He was doing all those things most of the time so that none of the girls would be interested in paying him a visit in his house. He was brilliant and his exploits in sports made him the toast of some pretty girls in his high school. Some girls who wanted to know his house when they were in junior classes failed due to his methodical faking of one excuse or the other.

He once told one of the girls when she kept pestering him to take her to his house, "Sorry, my father is a dangerous man, no one jokes with him. He is so traditional and hates all this modern-day boyfriend/girlfriend idea like shit. He's warned me never to be part of this stupidity. So, you can see why I've got to be careful. I can take a girl to any of my friends' houses whose parents aren't all that conventional like my dad. All these parents look at things differently."

"You're right Tayọ, there are some parents like that. I think they just want the best for their children which isn't bad," the girl said. Still, many of the ladies often teased him that he was a *ghost* with no known address.

One day, Tayọ went to town and met Bunmi on his way. She was his former Form 3 classmate. She failed the promotion examination to Form 4 and she was asked to repeat the class. She was one of the *ajẹbọta* students in their school. Her parents could have decided to take her to another school to complete her education if they had wanted. She was tall, curvy, beautiful, gentle and jovial.

"Tayọ Tayọ," she shouted.

"Ah.…. Ah, Bunmi, *oju ẹ ree.*[1] *Ọmọ ẹlẹ*[2] to sure. So, *na your face be this?*[3] You're looking good."

"Thank you Tayọ and stop being playful. Where are you going? What are you up to in my area?"

"I'm going to buy something in town."

"Do you live around here Bunmi?"

"Not quite far from here. If you're not in a hurry, we can stroll down to my house."

"Sure? I'm not in any hurry but even if I am…. em…., but your parents? Won't they chase me away?" Deep down, he was thrilled that Bunmi asked him to come and know where she lived.

"Don't worry about that. They trust me as I don't move with bad boys. In fact, they always encourage me to be wary of boys and face my studies more seriously after I had failed the promotion exam to Form 4."

"That must have been painful for you."

"Initially it was. To be honest with you, I couldn't sleep well or go out of our home for few weeks until my dad and mum appealed to me to see failure as part of learning. Their advice sank in. Now, I believe my future is brighter. I hail you the *efikos*[4] in our class at that time."

"Don't mind us. It was tough for us too, but we just managed to put in some extra efforts to make sure we got the needed results."

"Tayọ, you always take active part in school sports and you still perform well in your studies. How do you combine these two so well, sorry, I can't understand?"

"That's a good question, unfortunately, I don't have any proper answer for it. What happens is this. At times, I think I'm playing too much. Some other times, I think I'm spending too much time on my studies. I don't know how I do well on both sides. I don't know maybe that answers your question. 'B' for Bunmi. On as serious note, you're looking fresh as a daisy, what's the secret?" he teased her to change the topic.

"Thank you. No secret. It's God's work. Just learning to give myself rest of mind. Unlike before, nothing troubles me anymore."

"That's good to hear. I hope I can be like you. How are you coping with your studies?"

"I'm getting things right these days. We are coming behind you," she replied.

"How do you mean?"

"Don't worry about that. You know what I mean, you're now my senior though we started high school together."

"Don't trouble yourself Bunmi. We'll all still meet at the top later in life, right?"

"Hum…. think you're correct. Tayọ, we'll soon get to my house. That building painted white is the one."

"You mean that big two-storeyed building?" he responded with amazement.

"Yes. But, why that question?"

"And you said your parents won't mind me coming into their house in your company?"

"They won't. Believe me. Aren't you a man Tayọ?"

"I know for sure, I am, em….em….But when it comes to dealing with the rich people, you've got to watch it. Some of my friends have had raw deals from few moneybags just because they wanted to be close to their daughters. Well, in any case, let's go in. Let's go."

"I know what you're talking about but my parents aren't like some other rich people. They won't embarrass you. I'm assuring you."

"Fine. We will soon see. Where do they work?" he stopped and asked her for further clarification.

"My father was once a banker. My mother is a senior nurse in one of these government hospitals," Bunmi, who could still see fear written all over Tayọ, answered with pride.

"But, are you sure they will not embarrass me?"

"Don't worry. If they will, I wouldn't have invited you. Ṣebí[5] they're my parents. I am the one who invited you, isn't that right?"

They proceeded. When they got to the compound entrance, Bunmi pressed the alert button, the gatekeeper opened the gate for them. As they got into the premises, their brown

German Shepherd was barking ceaselessly in its cage. Not minding the dog, she informed their gatekeeper that Tayọ was a friend.

"What about the barking dog?" he stopped for few seconds looking at Bunmi for a quick answer.

"The dog is right inside its manger. Don't be afraid, just come with me, no problem for both of us," she said. She went to the manger door and said to the dog, "Raph, keep quiet. This is my guest." The dog kept quiet at once, wagged its tail and looked lovingly at Bunmi.

Tayọ, who was dumbfounded at the short scenario said silently, "Hum….em….This is serious!"

"Are you talking to me Tayọ?"

"No. Never mind. Em…."

Bunmi tried to open the entrance door to the big building but it was locked. She pressed the bell; their house girl came and opened the door. She greeted Tayọ with respect. Once in their well-furnished sitting room, Bunmi politely asked him to sit down. She took excuse and went upstairs. Tayọ looked at the housemaid and immediately remembered the time he was a house boy as if it were the previous day. He wanted to ask the girl how she was feeling as a house help but he thought that would be foolish and hasty. In a matter of minutes, the girl brought out two bottles of soft drink from the refrigerator, put them in a saucer and placed it on a stool beside his seat.

"Thank you," he said.

Bunmi came back with her photo album. "Sorry dear, I went to change my dress and also inform my parents that I'm at home with a friend."

The word "dear" was a music in his ears. As they were going through her family photo album, her parents came down. Tayọ nearly ran away out of fear. Their appearance was intimidating in that they both looked majestic.

"Dad and Mum, please meet Tayọ Kọlapọ, my school assistant senior prefect. We were once in the same class but he is a year ahead of me now. He is a member of our school football team. He is also an *efiko*.[6] He used to blow our heads off with big English words when we were in Form 1 and he's now one of our school's representatives in literary and debating competition with other schools."

Tayọ prostrated himself before Bunmi's parents and said, "Good afternoon, sir."

"Good day to you, young man. Bunmi has said so much about you just now. Incredible. Nice to hear all this coming from your school mate. Are you enjoying the post of assistant senior prefect of your school?"

"Sir, please don't mind Bunmi. Thank you, sir. Yes, I'm trying my best to enjoy it," he said still standing up as a sign of respect for Bunmi's parents.

"Sit down and feel at home. It's unusual for our daughter to invite someone to this house," Bunmi's mum said.

"Mum, not really. I just don't enjoy doing that."

"Yes, I know. And you just supported what I said. Tayọ, do you live around here?"

"No, Mummy, he doesn't," Bunmi cut in.

"She's correct ma. I live very close to our school."

"Good," her mother said.

"Well, that's all right. My advice is that all of you should make sure you face your studies. Make hay while the sun shines. Geoffrey Chaucer once said, 'Time and tide wait for no man.' Education is the light that illuminates the mind and body. There is nothing you can compare to it. Education first, other things later. Some of us your parents may be rich, don't be carried away by how rich we are and don't allow our wealth to distract you from working hard for your own money. *Ohun ti a ko ba jiya fun ki i pẹ lọwọ ẹni.*"[7] Bunmi's father said as he stood up to take his leave.

"Thank you, sir, we will do our best," both said.

They both continued looking through the photo album. He asked her many questions based on the beautiful and informative photo album. She proudly explained everything about her family to him. When it was time for him to leave, he told her to thank her parents on his behalf and thanked her for her hospitality.

"Sorry Tayọ, we don't do it that way in this family. My parents knew when you came, they will come down to say bye to you."

"But is that necessary?"

"Yes, it is. It'll be a sign of disrespect if I fail to notify them that you're about to go," she said on her way out of the living room.

Her parents came back and bid him goodbye. He thanked them and Bunmi and Tayọ left the house. Once outside their premises, he regained his full composure. Throughout his stay, he was not really sure whether her parents meant what they said. He was very happy for what her father said about the importance of education in one's life.

On the way to the bus stop, Bunmi said, "Tayọ, you are welcome here anytime."

"Are you sure, did I hear you well, fine girl?"

"Yes, very sure."

"Thank you. 'B' for Bunmi."

"If you won't mind, I'll come to your house one of these days," she said jovially.

"Who am I to mind hosting an August visitor like you, even if you decide to come in October or December? If you would like to come, I dare not, beautiful girl."

"Ha….ha….ha….ha (she laughs). Boys and their sugar-coated mouth! Some of you would lie to us that your fathers own Wembley Stadium or the National Stadium or The White House or Number 10 Downing Street when they don't even own an apartment of any known address. One other curious thing I've found out about many boys is that, they never lied their mothers owned anything. Isn't that correct but ridiculous? It's always: 'My dad or my father or my popsi[8] or my papa or my grandpa or my great grandpa owns this or that! Is it that their mothers don't work or own anything of significance? Hum…. boys!"

As she said this, they both burst into laughter and Tayọ responded, "Sorry, Bunmi, I'm not one of them though. I hate lying. Trust me. I know many guys fit your description perfectly well. Hum…."

"Hum…. Sure? I'll wait and see. Girls, we need to be careful of accepting anything guys say. But don't worry Tayọ. Just give me your address and I'll give you a surprise visit."

He promised to give her his address when they got back to school the following week. With that promise, they parted ways. All that happened that day was like a dream to him because he and Bunmi were not close when they were in the same class. He was always thinking about that chance meeting with her but his next big problem was where to host her if she decided to come as she had promised. He thought of some beautiful homes of his friends to take her to but which one and how to organise it as if it was really

his own house were the major problems. They met the
following Monday in school and exchanged greetings very
warmly.

"Thanks for the invitation of the other day. How are your
dad and mum doing?"

"Tayọ, don't mention. Thanks for coming too. They are
both fine. Daddy said this morning on his way out that I
should greet you."

"Em.…. are you sure or you're just pulling my leg? Well, your
parents are different from most of the rich parents I know. I
must confess. I thought I would land in a police cell that
day. Sure."

"But I guaranteed you that there was nothing to worry
about as far as my parents were concerned. I know them
well and they know me well. Let's put that aside for now.
Remember I promised I would be in your house any time
you give me your address, still remember? Yes?"

"I'm not all that forgetful Lady B. Do you have any
particular day in mind when you would like to come?" he
asked in order to perfect his strategy of where to host her.

"I can't tell you yet, but definitely, I will, after I've taken
permission from my parents."

"You mean your parents will allow you to come and
visit me?"

"Pretty sure, they won't mind, Tayọ."

"Okay, first ask them and get back to me then."

"No problem. Very soon I will. Love you. Thank you Tayọ."

From that day, their casual relationship metamorphosed into a romantic friendship. During break time each day, she would wait for him near their school lunchroom. They always bought their food and ate together. Many times, she would squeeze some money into his hand to pay for whatever they bought. They were soon nick-named Romeo and Juliet. Neither of them paid any attention to rumours circulating around about the two of them. Some students said he had used *juju* on her. Others said she just wanted to put him in problem as her influential parents would deal with him when they got to know what he was up to with their daughter.

When school closed one day, Tayọ saw Bunmi off before he went home. Her parents' driver did not come to pick her up. He went to his family house straight from school as it was already late and he did not want to go to any of his friends' homes. Once he got home, he quickly changed from his school uniform and put on a casual shirt and shorts. He took a plate and headed for a foodshed nearby to buy cooked beans to eat with soaked *garri*[9] popularly called garrium sulphate[10] by students from poor families. It was their own balanced diet. Just about few metres away from his family house and at a very sharp corner, he came face-to-face with Bunmi and her friend, Rachael. He was dazed and confused. He could not at first open his mouth to even say ordinary 'hello'. He thought it was a bad dream. He wanted to lie but he could not get the appropriate lie to tell at that very moment. Rachael, Bunmi's friend said, "I told you, he lives around here though I didn't know the exact house." Tayo wished the ground should open and swallow him up.

"Tayọ, hope you're okay. Why are you not happy to see us? We just tried our luck to see if you live around here as Rachael thought," Bunmi said calmly.

"Sorry, it isn't that. I'm like, em….em….em….I didn't know you know this place, Rachael."

"Not really, but our family house is somewhere around here. It's one of the few best houses in this slum area. Thanks to my parents who rebuilt the traditional house into a modern edifice for my grandparents. I believe you'll know the house I'm talking about. I have seen you one or two times when I came with my parents to see my grandparents. But you didn't notice I was the one both times. Well, are you ok?" she asked.

"Surprise, surprise Tayọ. I told you I would be in your house one day but I didn't want you to know the exact day. I seized this opportunity when it came. Rachael told me few weeks ago that she probably knew where you live," Bunmi said as if she did not hear her friend's boasting about her grandparents' home.

"But em....em....Rachael, how frequently do you come to this area?" Tayọ said incoherently feeling the excruciating agony of helplessness.

"No. Not frequently at all. Seems you're going to buy something, right?" Rachael changed the topic and reminded him of his mission.

"Maybe that's why you appear so casual," Bunmi added.

"Don't mind me. My uncle sent me to quickly buy some cooked beans for him to eat with soaked *garri*. He loves it a lot," Tayọ said and they all laughed.

"Can we wait for you here then? Go and buy the cooked beans, and we could then go back to your house together."

"Mo kú."[11] He did not know when that statement came out of his mouth.

"What did you say now?" the girls asked.

"Did I say something? Sorry, don't worry. I'll go later to buy it but....em....my father is around but em....em...."

"But if your dad is at home, you can introduce us as your school mates, can't you? Moreover, we are still in school uniform," Bunmi reasoned wisely.

"Let's go. No problem," he said as he accepted he had been caught pants down and there was no way out of the coming humiliation.

262

He was ready to face the consequences of taking the two
beauties to his shanty. He knew the worst that could happen
was for Bunmi to dump him and probably tell her parents
that his home and area were not supposed to be inhabited
by human beings. He recognised how much most rich
people detested the underprivileged. They went to his
ghetto walking carefully not to fall into the dirty drains that
dotted the way. They entered the house but nobody was in.

"Where is this?" Rachael asked.

"Rachael, take it easy, ah…ah! Your mouth won't kill you,"
Bunmi said.

"Sorry girls. This is where I'm managing to live for now
because of certain issues I had with my dad and one of his
wives recently. I moved here just last week. Don't be
surprised, my dad is a polygamist. He's married with many
wives because he is a typical African man. Women just love
him and he loves them too."

"But your dad isn't rich, is he?" Rachael asked.

"He was, sorry, he is, I think, em….em….This is our family
house, em….em….mind you, not his."

Since there was no single chair in his room or a bed, he
reluctantly brought out his multi-purpose mat. His mat
served two main purposes: to sit and sleep on. He spread it
on the floor for them to sit. There was no electricity supply
but a small opened window allowed limited light into the
room during the day. As they sat down on the mat, he was

terribly worried. There was terrible heat from the roofing sheet and the window did not allow much air inside as the houses in the area were built wall to wall.

"This type of house is common in my father's village. I saw many of them each time we went there. But my dad has built a modern house in the village for his parents with a borehole and a generator to supply them water and light. My father often told us how he managed to cope with this type of environment when he was young like us. He always tells us we should count ourselves lucky with the life we live these days. But Tayọ, how do you manage to study at night, I can understand in the daytime but…? You must have a very good brain."

"You mean your dad once lived in a place like this, Bunmi?" he dodged her question.

"Yes. Yes. I think his own was even worse. That's why I don't look down on people living in a place you think is less habitable. There are many reasons why that could happen according to my dad. Moreover, things can change for them and they may end up living in a palace tomorrow, can't they? My dad's case is a good example."

"Really? Hum…. Good talk, Bunmi, I'm learning something I've not been told before," Rachael said.

"This is interesting," Tayọ said when he recovered his calmness and then asked, "Now, what will you girls take? Please, feel free to dine with me this afternoon."

"We can't take anything. We must be going now. It's nice knowing where you live," Bunmi said.

"Please, you need to take something, or are you angry with me?" he pleaded with them though he did not have any money to buy them even a bottle of Coca-Cola. Their rejection of being entertained was a prayer answered in a way.

"Not at all. My parents will be wondering why I've kept so late coming back home by now," Bunmi said.

"Well, thanks for your surprise but fruitful visit. You have made my day. I hope you'll come back again, won't you?"

"Definitely yes, if you want us to," both replied.

Throughout the rest of the day, Tayo was not himself. He had double feelings.

"Why did these girls do this to me? This is embarrassing. I may be the topic for discussion in our school now.... Oh my.... That Rachael especially!" He thought over the impression both girls would have created about him and his shabby environment but he was thankful at the same time that Bunmi took everything calmly and saved him the immediate much-anticipated embarrassment. He felt humiliated as he dozed off on his mat.

"Where have you been, Bunmi? You're a bit late today. I hope there's no...."

"Sorry Dad. Nothing to worry about. You know what Dad? One of my friends, Rachael and myself paid Tayọ a surprised visit."

"And?"

"Nothing Dad. It's just that he lives in his family house. The area isn't all that nice. Where he lives resembles one of those houses in our grandparents' village. I told him about your own life at the beginning of your life which you always tell us was terrible. About where you used to live, how you walked miles to and from school, how difficult it was for you getting water to use, how you dealt with mosquitoes during the night, how you used lanterns to study and so on."

"Ha…. ha…. ha (her father laughs). Good you still remember all those things. In short, you encouraged him not to feel bad?"

"Exactly, Dad."

"That's my daughter. It's good to tell all of you, our children, stories about how we and our own parents and their grandparents started life before we got to where we are today. Some of us might be very rich at present. Yes. But at one time or the other, it must have been very bumpy and tough coping with life. This might be because of poverty, rejection, illness, lack of academic abilities, parents' separation, mistakes made, government unfair policies, sudden downturn in business ventures etc, etc. None of these should however stop a determined person from becoming something or somebody in life. But, was he happy to see you?"

"At first, no. He was in a state of shock. Rachael did not help matter either."

"I expected that. I've been there before. Well, a good experience you've had today then?"

"Yes, Dad. You know what? I always admire the way you and my mum see things in life. I hope I and others could always see things the same way too."

"Don't worry. We can already see some of our attitudes in you and we're happy for this."

CHAPTER THIRTEEN

G ood things come to those who believe, better things come to those who are patient and the best things come to those who don't give up - Unknown

When Tayọ was in Form 5 and towards the end of his high school education, a multi-national company in Nigeria organised a competitive written examination for high school students in the country. They promised to award scholarships to successful candidates especially those in science-oriented subjects: physics, chemistry, biology and mathematics which Nigerian students popularly referred to as *phychembi & maths*. They liaised with the education ministry of each region. The ministry directed that each school should present three students who they believed were their best students. When the circular reached Origbo High School, the principal called a staff meeting where the modality for the selection of their school's candidates was

agreed. Two students from Form 5 and one from Form 4
were selected based on their previous performances in all
internal and external examinations they had taken. One of
the Form 5 students chosen was Tayọ. The school organised
extra coaching for the students and they were ordered to
come to school during the weekends to get fully prepared
for the competitive test. Apart from their school's
determination to make sure they excelled, Tayọ went the
extra mile. For him, passing the test and getting the
scholarship was a do or die affair. He thought he was about
to get back what he lost in primary school when he failed to
get the required mark to be considered for scholarship. He
used some central nervous stimulant drug that aids
attentiveness and wakefulness which he bought from a
pharmacy. This made him go without sleep for hours and
days. He just studied and did some sports. It got to a stage
that even if he desired to sleep, he was not able to. He did
not tell anyone about that because he assumed he was
coping well and that after the scholarship test, he would
sleep as much as possible. The date for the scholarship
written exam was fixed. Unfortunately, Tayọ had
overprepared hoping that the offer must not be missed
again. He did not suffer from performance mentality so he
thought all was fine with him. In the class one day, just
about a week to the test, he fainted. He was taken to the
hospital unconscious. The result of his blood sample
showed he had taken some sleep-deprivation drugs which
had affected his body clock badly. He confirmed the
doctor's findings and pleaded with them to save his life.

That misjudgement shocked him and he thought later, *"What ill-luck is this? Why me again? This must be a big joke! Why now? Um.... This life. Did I really undo myself? Maybe this scholarship of a thing would have sorted my future once and for all, who knows? Now that education is no more free, what a luck that might have been for me if I had sat the test and passed. Would I ever go to university anymore?"*

He thought about those issues many times. The doctors advised him not to think too much over what had happened if he really wanted to recuperate. They told him that many things happened for some certain purposes. The school asked his father to come for a meeting. He came and he was briefed on what happened to his son. He felt very bad but he was assured that all would be well with his son. He and Dupẹ visited him in the hospital few times. His teachers, classmates and school representatives who called on him in the hospital also advised him not to see what happened to him as the end of life. Bunmi was also very sympathetic and anxious about his health. He told her each time that he would come out of it stronger. She informed him on one of her visits that she had told her parents about his hospitalisation and they promised to come and see him.

One afternoon, her Dad came to see him. After greetings, he said, "Tayọ, sorry to hear what happened. How are you getting on? It's really a pity that things have turned out this way for you. I know it can be very painful. You need to take it like that and get yourself ready for what your future has got in store for you. You should know that what's coming is better than what's gone. Moreover, good things often happen when you least expect them. Cheer up to aid your recuperation."

"Thank you, sir, for your visit. I am getting better every day. I will try everything possible to come out of this my present sad situation."

Bunmi's father left after some few minutes. Tayọ could not understand how such an important person could find time to come and wish him well. His coming alone brought fresh hope to him. Once he was discharged from the hospital, he paid Bunmi's parents a visit to thank them for their moral support. They were happy to see him feeling healthy and happy again. Bunmi was not at home that day.

"Tayọ, well done for your spirit of 'can do' you have adopted so far after that attempt to possibly get a scholarship failed. When there is life, there is hope. We have good news for you from this end, I mean from our family. This is the good news. My family have decided to give you a scholarship to study any course you want to study in any part of the world provided you can make your papers at one sitting. However, no pressure this time round. I want to believe you have learnt your lesson. What you need to do is study well but, don't study to the extent of ending up in hospital again. Plan your time for everything you want to do from now. Time to study. Time to play. And, time to sleep well. You should not neglect social connectedness and physical activity. These are very important. Never take any drug to aid your mental performance. A note of warning: you don't need to tell anyone about this offer until everything works out fine. Why? It's just to make sure you don't put yourself under unnecessary burden once more. Bunmi had been informed but she was warned not to tell you until we break the news to you. Bear it in mind that what you went through was one of the uncertainties of life. Note this, when one door closes, another one opens. Don't give up hope," he concluded.

"Sir, but…. em….Did I hear you…..em….Thank you so much sir. This is good news indeed. Again, unexpected! This is hard for me to believe. In fact, I am short of words. Thank you again and again for your concern and this offer of scholarship. Sir, I promise to do my best in my final examination."

He met Bunmi on his way out of their premises and asked why she didn't tell him the news her father had just told him. She laughed and said, "Tayọ, don't mind me. *It's keep our secret secret* as we often say in my family. That's what I was asked to do. All was well planned and executed. Love you and, all the best."

Few weeks after Tayọ had been discharged from the hospital, an officer from the ministry of education came to his school to see the principal. Both had a closed-door meeting. Immediately the ministry staff left, the principal called a staff meeting where he informed his teachers of the new development regarding the scholarship test which Tayọ missed due to his illness. He also sent for and passed the new message from the ministry to him. He was very glad to hear the news.

The following morning when the assembly was almost coming to an end, the principal said, "One more significant news to tell you." The students who were anxious to know what that might be, were all ears.

"This is good news for Tayọ, for this school and for all of us," the principal started. "Life is not made up of smooth highways. At times, you must fumble and wobble to reach your destination. At times, you may get to where you're going very smoothly, but I must add, that seldom happens. Am I making some sense here?"

"You are, sir."

"If you all still remember, the ministry of education organised a competitive scholarship test for some brilliant students some time ago in partnership with a multi-national company. One of our students, Tayọ, took ill before the test and could not write the exam. We have been expecting the result ever since for those who sat the test but none has come so far. Yesterday, a staff from the ministry of education came to my office to inform me that all those who missed the test due to one reason or the other, and whose cases were genuine had been reconsidered to take the test in order to be fair to all the applicants." Tayọ listened attentively as the principal continued to confirm what he had been told.

"So, Tayọ has now got another chance to participate in what we all thought was a lost prospect. We are highlighting this issue to tell all of you that, whatever in life that comes your way, bad or good, try to see it as what is meant to happen to you at that point in time. The test will take place next Thursday and we have been promised the result would be out the following week. We wish our representatives the best of luck," the principal ended his long speech.

Tayọ, knowing he just had a few days to prepare for the test, took everything with ease, coupled with the fact that Bunmi's father's offer was also on the table. He went for the test and did his best. He was not too apprehensive about the result. The following week as promised, the result was released. The school was informed that only 35 out of more than 200 students that sat the test satisfied the scholarship requirements. Among those, only 30 got full scholarship while the rest got partial scholarship. The principal told the students this on the assembly.

"It is *ojoro*[1] sir. Let's forget it. Why not 50 or 80 students out of more than 200 students?" one of the Form 5 students shouted from the back as others laughed.

"Silence please. Total silence," the principal cried out. "But *ojoro* or no *ojoro*, *magomago*[2] or no magomago, I have with me here the authentic documents confirming that Lere, our social prefect and Tayọ, our assistant senior prefect have both been granted full scholarship awards."

"Hip hip hip hooray. Hip hip hooray," one student screamed. The rest over-joyous students shouted in frenzy, "Hip hip hip hooray."

"Silence. Order. That's perfectly okay. It's good to rejoice with others when good things come their way. But it's with regret that one of our students did not get the award. However, there's always another time as we've been telling all of you."

"Yes. Yes," the students replied.

"Just to let you also know. The company has concluded that ten more students would be given scholarships every year for the next five years. What this means is that all of you, once you can face your studies, are potential scholarship winners. It's a matter of time."

"Yes sir. This is wonderful. Good news for all of us," one of the students yelled.

"On a more serious note, this is a big lesson for all of you. You don't need to give up the struggle. It may be that, at the point when you're giving up is when your breakthrough is just around the corner. I asked, if Tayọ had died or had run mad recently, if he had given up on his academic work as he once tempted to do, would this offer come his way now? It is then true that a true winner is he who endures till the end. Tayọ Kọlapọ, Lere Ganiyu, could you please come out and receive your scholarship awards. Both of you are our worthy ambassadors. Please, give them a round of applause." They both came out proudly and collected their prizes."

"Lere, Tayọ, this is not the end of the journey. You have to see this as a beginning of another trip you're going in life. As you've known, you will still need to pass your final exam at very high credit level to scale the final hurdle which I hope will not be a problem for both of you. All members of staff and students of this great school wish both of you all the best."

"Thank you very much sir. Thank you all," both students took their documents, bowed and left the stage. Immediately the assembly was dismissed.

When the school closed for the day and Tayọ and Bunmi were alone, Bunmi said, "Tayọ, you've made me and my parents proud of you. My dad mentions you as an example of doggedness in the face of adversity. So does my mum too. Two options are now before you, and I know for sure you're destined for greatness but will you promise me you're going to take things easy."

"Yes Bunmi, I promise I will. I've learnt my lesson in a hard way that, God's time is the best. Thank you."

Bunmi replied, "You're welcome Tayọ. Each time I remember my first visit to your family house in company with Rachael, I admire your strong character. Many of us would have complained to the high heaven about our circumstances if we were in your shoes. I'm doing my best academically, but I don't think I can ever become an *efiko*[3] like you."

"Thank you again. I appreciate you and I appreciate your parents. You told them everything about me. They are not put off by my background or say anything to make me feel inferior. Whoa! It's unbelievable. Rich people like your parents, we all know, hardly ever want their children to be friends with the children of the poor. So, they wouldn't ever encourage them to be with them in a loving relationship. I'm learning something new from them and I hope I won't mess up with such knowledge. You have shown me that you're a very dependable girl in and out. The first time I was reluctant to follow you to your house, you said something I will never forget."

"What did I say, I've forgotten em….em…."

"Just let me paraphrase it. You said I should not worry because your parents knew you and that you knew them very well. What a mutual trust between you and your parents! Your family have become another Godsent in my tortuous journey through life. How lucky can I be?"

"That's too good of you. That's just us in my family. Keep up with all you're doing right, your future and my future will…."

"…be wonderful together," he completed the sentence for her.

"Amen," she said.

Tayọ informed everyone who he sincerely believed should hear about his scholarship award success. Those included Mrs Aka's family, Bunmi's parents, his own father, Dupẹ, Ikẹ, Uncle Ezekiel who had stood with them like The Rock of Gibraltar and Uncle Sunday who introduced him to Mrs Aka. He specifically showed his appreciation to Mr Aliu for being such a wonderful encourager and teacher.

The following weeks, he burned the midnight oil in preparation for his final WAEC exams in which he registered for nine subjects. When the result was released, he had 1A and 8As* which qualified him to further his education on scholarship at the University of Glasgow in Scotland where he had applied to study medicine. The multi-national company that awarded Tayọ scholarship made sure all arrangements regarding his departure from Nigeria and his stay in Scotland were first-rate.

On the day Tayọ was leaving Nigeria for Scotland, Bunmi's parents, Uncle Ezekiel, Dayọ, Dupẹ, Ikẹ, Bunmi, Tayọ's father, Mr Aliu and Mrs Aka came to the Murtala Muhammed International Airport in Lagos with him. They all left Ibadan at 6am for his 11 pm flight. The 126.6-long Lagos-Ibadan expressway journey that should have taken them less than two hours to cover took them eight hours because some Christian and Muslim religious bodies whose praying grounds dotted everywhere along the express way were having their usual marathon prayer meetings. Travellers on the expressway at times did spend twelve hours on the road if they were unlucky to come across

motor accidents coupled with the usual prayer meetings.
The presence of those religious camps on the popular
expressway had divided opinions among Nigerians who
read religious meanings into everything going on in their
country. Tayọ and his well-wishers took into consideration
the traffic logjam usually experienced almost daily on the
highway before they departed for Lagos and they were not
proved wrong. Eventually they all got to the airport looking
very tired. Bunmi, was melancholic that Tayo was leaving
her. If she had had a choice, she would have preferred that
he studied in Nigeria.

"I'm very sad that you're leaving me behind," she said with
teary eyes when the two of them were alone.

"I know. Same with me. But this is what you've wanted for
me. This is what your parents want for me. This is what I
have laboured for quite a long time to get. This is what I
almost lost my life for. This is what my family want for me
too. Let me do it. Very soon, I'll be done with my studies.
This will be over in few years' time. I'll come back to this
country and we'll meet again to part no more. Come on.
Stop crying. Give me a hug and wish me all the best. It's
very hard for the two of us but we've got to manage the
situation well. Cheer up 'B' for Bunmi," he said. When she
stopped crying and got composed, he advised her to face
her studies and to continue to be a good girl. Both Romeo
and Juliet shed tears when it was the last time to say
goodbye to each other. But it is true that, people will always
meet to part and part to meet.

CHAPTER FOURTEEN

Education is the most powerful weapon you can use to change the world – Nelson Mandela

Táyọ's first-time air travel went swimmingly on a KLM Boeing 777 200 plane. The plane was like a moving three-star hotel in the air when the journey started, it was so stable in the air that Táyọ at one time forgot he was on a plane. From Amsterdam where the plane had a stop-over, the story changed as the weather became turbulent and at a point, it was as if the plane would crash. The situation was so chaotic that frequent fliers also felt quite uneasy. With his Bible in his hands, Tayọ neither knew what Psalm to read nor what Bible verse to recite though he tried to. He also wanted to pray but he could not utter a word. Palpable fear was written all over him. When he became helpless and confused, he closed his eyes tightly and began to tell God silently, *"God Almighty, You have seen me this far, please don't*

leave me to die today. I left Nigeria with joy, let my joy be full.
Help me this time again. You have seen me through so many
troubles in life. Take me to Scotland safely. All of us on this plane
need your protection Lord Jesus of Nazareth. Please help the plane
crew to get it right. Please God, help all of us. No. No.
Pleeeeaaaaseeeeeeee God. Help me, pleeeaaaaaaseee, help us.
Don't let today be my final day on earth."

Some people on the plane were shouting while others were
praying aloud in tongues as the flight pilot was trying to
reassure everyone that all would soon be well. After about
one hour, the weather stabilised and the atmosphere on the
plane was calm. Everybody was happy. Shortly after, some
started to chat loudly and drink alcohol to Tayọ's surprise
because he was still unable to get himself round what
happened. The flight attendants went round picking up
serving plates, cups and other items while some of them
served those who requested for one thing or the other.
Many passengers wanted to use the plane toilets and that
caused a queue. Tayọ was glued to his seat like a robot
though he also needed the toilet. He just wanted the plane
to land so he could get out and give glory to God for His
protection over all of them. When the pilot announced that
the plane was getting ready to land and asked everyone to
be seated and put their seatbelt on, he heaved a sigh of
relief. The sight of some of the UK geographical area from
the plane up in the sky was captivating. He looked and
looked from his window seat and was happy that the
beautiful country he had read so much about was before

him. When the plane taxied to a stop, many passengers quickly collected their hand baggage on their way out waiting for the plane doors to open. Tayọ did not join the rush. He remained seated, closed his eyes and thanked God for the journey mercy. When almost everyone had left, he exited the plane.

The university representatives on ground at the airport gave him a warm welcome and made his onward movement to his hotel easy. Immediately he had his shower and ate his food, he fell asleep and woke up ten hours later. That week, he was made to feel at home by the staff and students at the university. The academic and non-academic matters were thoroughly explained to all the freshers.

For him to become an ophthalmologist, he firstly completed a degree in medicine and obtained a MBBS. After that, he got his Master of Surgery (M. S.) in ophthalmology. He did his three-year residency in ophthalmology following his one-year internship. The course was one of the most intellectually taxing areas of medicine as an ophthalmologist needed a strong mastery of all human body systems and of clinical medicine to do well in the field. He knew what he came to achieve at the University of Glasgow and he went all out for it. He did not combine frivolity with his serious business of academic excellence. He won many prizes for the various research works he carried out on eye problems especially the kind of problems that affected people in Africa and some other Third World countries.

One day, Bunmi's father was reading an article in an international newspaper titled: *Britain May Soon Run Out of Ophthalmic Surgeons.* He carefully read the lengthy article on various issues raised by the writer. Once on a phone call to Tayọ, he asked him, "Tayọ, what makes your area of studies so difficult that majority of students in Britain are not enrolling into the course?"

"Why did you ask that question sir?"

"I was reading an interesting article on that topic some weeks back which raised my curiosity."

"That's great sir. It isn't a straightforward question. We all know the eye is one of the most complex parts of the human body. In ophthalmology, we detect and treat all eye diseases, perform eye surgery and prescribe and fit eyeglasses and contact lenses to rectify vision problems. Many of us are also involved in scientific research on the causes and cures for eye disease and vision disorders. Here in the UK, the course is one of the most competitive specialties. To tell you how competitive it is in the UK, an average gross annual salary for an ophthalmologist is £95,000. Added to that is an average bonus of £5,000 whereas a GP's salary might be in the range of £55,000 depending on experience."

"Hum, your answer is illuminating. So, tough course, competitive course, great salary!"

"Something like that sir."

When he finished his studies, he mooted the idea of staying over in Britain where Bunmi would have come and joined him but Bunmi's parents advised him against doing that. They promised to assist him to get settled in Nigeria once he came back. He took to their advice and worked for some years in the UK to get some savings. During his long sojourn in the UK, both Tayọ and Bunmi kept in touch regularly. Bunmi, during that time, also completed her course in International Business Management to the joy of her parents who had always wanted one of their children to manage their business empire one day. Twice, her parents sponsored her trip to Scotland to holiday with Tayọ.

He finally returned to the country to settle down and practise as he had promised. His coming back was much more glorious than when he left. Many people came to the airport to welcome him back. He was taken to a well-furnished accommodation in Ikọlaba, one of the nicest places to live in Ibadan which Bunmi, her parents and Uncle Ezekiel had got ready for him.

The time of his arrival in Nigeria marked a new era in the medical history of the country. His area of specialisation, ophthalmology, was very important in that, hitherto, many people lost their sight because of common eye problems which could easily be treated. He teamed up with the government and other health professionals in his area of expertise to find a definite way to tackle eye problems especially among the elderly in Africa. Alongside that, he set up his own eye specialist hospital, *TayBun Eye Specialist*

Clinic, in Mọkọla, an upscale part in Ibadan City which was just a short distance from the University College Hospital (UCH) Ibadan and the popular Premier Hotel. That was made possible with his own savings and financial support from Bunmi's parents. It was a standard medical centre in every sense. The surgery became well-known very quickly in Nigeria and internationally. It thrived because of its strong foundation and expertise of the eye surgeons who worked there. Many wealthy African people who used to travel overseas to treat eye problems found out that the same standard of care they got in foreign countries was available in *TayBun* health centre. He identified and treated poor patients free of charge and that endeared him to a lot of people all over the country.

Two years after he came back to Nigeria, he proposed to Bunmi, who had been appointed as a director in her father's business portfolio. She accepted his proposal. They fixed their nuptial date. Preparations for the wedding started at once. Bunmi's parents were so pleased with both of them and they did everything possible to assist them in every needed area.

On their wedding day, Mrs Aka, Uncle Ezekiel, Tayọ's father, Mr Aliu, Dayọ, Bunmi's father and some of their friends were each given a very short time to say something they knew about the groom and the bride at the reception.

Mr Kọmọlafẹ, Tayọ's catechist in primary school and the main speaker for the day, was called upon to give his speech.

He stood up joyfully and said, "This is the day that the Lord has made. We must rejoice and be glad in it. Congratulations to these young couple on this special day. Many of you here may be thinking this Reverend is here to preach a sermon. No. I came here today not as a Reverend. I came here today as an encourager. Yes. I'm here today to give words of encouragement that will bless this new couple and everyone who is present here today. To start with, I have known Tayọ since he was in primary school. There are lots of things I can say here today about his humble background if time permits me. In a nutshell, I have come to realise again, that, just because your earlier life didn't turn out like you wanted it to, doesn't mean that your latter stage of life can't be better than you ever imagined. From all I have heard and known about this amiable young man, I believe that scars, which may be emotional, psychological, financial or physical, do heal. In fact, your scars can bring out the stars in you and at times, you have to go through the worst to get to the best. Great possibilities are encased in adversities. So, do not run away from tests of life.

"Back to the basic, Tayọ, Bunmi, both of you are coming into this union from different backgrounds. I appeal to you, make this marriage work. You can. You have both got all it takes to do this. Allow God, the Almighty, into your marriage. He is the originator of the marriage institution. Make Him the third person in your home. Respect each other. Serve each other. Look for the best in each other. Work together. Pray together. Worship together. Talk

together. Travel together. Joke together. Laugh together.
Cry together. Don't deny each other the conjugal rights as
God planned it for any holy union between a man and a
woman. Bring some God-filled perspective to things you do
daily in your family right from today. Someone once said,
'Your life becomes a masterpiece when you master peace'.
Please, let peace reign in your family. Look for peace. Work
for peace. Hold tightly to peace. Let peace dominate your
family affairs. Make every effort to keep the family unity,
for without it, nothing tangible can be achieved in life. If
you do all these devotedly, I believe many people would
learn a lot from you. I pray the Lord bless you with children
very soon. And in due course, we shall gather for another
celebration with your family. And so shall it be. Always
remember that you must let your marriage be founded on
the Rock.

"To all of you, dear well-wishers, I pray things of joy will
always be your portion in the mighty Name of our Lord
Jesus. I commit both of you into the mighty hands of the
Almighty God who is able to bless and keep you safe. It is
well with you today. It will be well with you tomorrow and
every day of your life. And everybody please say…."

Everybody stood up and shouted, "Amen. Amen. Amen," as
they gave the catechist a thunderous applause.

When everyone started wishing them the best of luck, both
the groom and the bride were shedding tears of joy. That
wedding day remained a Red-Letter Day for the couple.

They went for their honeymoon in Abuja, the capital city of Nigeria. Thus, they began their marital journey on a very solid foundation.

Tayọ was at home one evening when his security officer informed him that some people were around to see him. He told him to let them in. He opened the gate for the visitors. He greeted them with due respect and took them to the waiting room in one corner of the premises. He asked them to sit down. They were four in number, all men. He offered them some water and told them he would go and inform his ọ̀gá[1] if they could write their details in the visitor's book. After that, he took the visitor's book to Tayọ. He checked the details of the visitors and was surprised because he was not expecting such guests that day. He told the guard to take them to the meeting room and that he would join them there. He changed into another dress and asked his wife if she was aware some people were coming to see them that day but she said 'no'. He showed her the visitor's book to see the people that had come to meet him. He left her and went straight to the meeting room. He exchanged greetings with them and they all sat down.

"First, what can we offer you?"

"Doctor, we'll come to that bit later. As we often say, business before pleasure," everybody laughed at the man's joke.

"For the purpose of introduction," their speaker started, "This is High Chief (Dr.) Onadipe Sokunbi, permanent secretary, federal ministry of health. To his left is Prof. (Malam) Salim Bamangar Turaki Mohammed, an ophthalmologist at the Federal University Teaching Hospital, Ilobu (FUTHI). Next is Igwe (Honourable) (Dr.) Gburugburu Benjamin Okongwu, the executive personal assistant to the minister of health and my humble self, High Chief, Prof. (Emeritus) (Ordained Senior Pastor) Olaloju Oloruntobi Gbemugbemu, the chief medical director (M.D.) at FUTHI."

"You are all welcome. I'm Tayo Kolapo as you might have probably known. I'm an ophthalmic surgeon. But I hope I've not committed any serious crime that warrants you paying me this visit?"

"No, no Doctor," they all said as they laughed at his witticism.

"But Doctor, we're only here to arrest you for a good cause though," one of them said and they all laughed again.

"To start with, we are here to invite you to join our new ophthalmology department at FUTHI. Your revolutionary eye care service in this country is being talked about everywhere. We have also discussed your extraordinary exploit in this field many times. We all recognise the enormous work you are doing in that area of medicine. Therefore, the minister of health is planning to set up a special department for eye care for the elderly people in this country. That area has been a concern for the president himself. We have noted that some of our elderly people now travel overseas to have their eye problems corrected. Those who don't have the means are losing their sight at a very fast rate. The minister has discussed this issue with the president and he has given us the green light to do all it takes to make sure this becomes a reality as soon as practicable. He wants as many elderly people as possible to enjoy their sight till the end of their life."

"Thank you for this honour. It is one field in medicine I'm so much concerned with as I believe no one should lose his or her sight needlessly in this country anymore. If the research grant is made available, if facilities are there, if we're given an open hand to operate, if awareness is rigorously pursued and if we can gather notable names in the profession to work on full time or part time basis, people all over the world will soon be coming to our country for world-class eye care. It is my pleasure to accept this offer and we can start serious dialogue on all other related matters for the project."

"That's splendid Doctor. Next week, we will get in touch with you for a formal meeting which will come up soon at the ministry of health, Abuja. Thank you once again for your cooperation and for making this visit a success," their spokesman said.

Tayọ invited his wife to come and meet the visitors. After her introduction, the guests were fully entertained. He was given a direct number to the honourable minister of health who would give him a call after the outcome of their meeting might have been made known to him. He and his wife saw them off. When they came back in, he told her everything that took place during the meeting. She congratulated him on his new breakthrough. The following weekend, they went to see her parents. Both parents were watching a TV programme when they strolled in cheerfully.

"Good afternoon Daddy and Mummy *o yoyo,*" both said laughing.

"Good afternoon. The two of you are laughing as if you have just won a lottery. *Eyi wu wa o,*[2]" Bunmi's mother said looking straight into their eyes.

"Thanks. Mum, not lottery luck, but something bigger than lottery," she said.

"What could be more than winning a jackpot?" Bunmi's father asked.

"And when you don't play lottery, what happens dad?" Bunmi asked.

"Then you win nothing," Tayọ replied.

Bunmi first went to her mum's kitchen and brought some snacks for the family to enjoy. They sat down and Tayọ narrated his wonderful newest story to them.

"Whoa! Congratulations to you and your family. May the Lord always be with you. Wonderful God!" both parents chorused.

"Dad, I think this country is now waking up to its responsibility to the citizens. If this works as it's being planned, ordinary people will feel its direct impact," Tayọ said.

"We think that's how it should be if not that the past governments have made a mess of everything we used to be proud of in this country. Successive bad governments. Successive past policies. Successive bad results. But with this one coming directly from the presidency, all hope is not lost," Bunmi's dad summarised.

"We will get there eventually," her mum intoned.

"We pray for that Mum," Tayọ and Bunmi said.

A few weeks after that meeting, Tayọ got a call from the minister of health and they discussed various issues relating to the new project at length. They spoke on some topics that he had raised during the first meeting with the minister's representatives and urged the minister to make sure that the programme worked. Later, other meetings were held and the minister presented letters of appointment to all the staff of the new department. The government promised to go along with them on the modalities for the new health revolution. They promised them an open hand as they had requested.

Hardly had they started working however, when another military coup was staged in the country. It was a bloody one. The president and other top government officials lost their lives. The new regime removed all past ministers and discarded almost everything they had done or planned to do. The minister of health lost his job. The power change in the country killed the dream for a new eye care vision department for the elderly which the minister and his boss, the dead president, had wanted to champion. The military junta happily assassinated the president and his dream for a better Nigeria. Everything in the country was back to how it used to be – poor policies, corruption, subjugation, nepotism at the highest level, draconian decrees, poor governance, and mission without vision. Tayọ went back to his private practice and he continued to prosper.

CHAPTER FIFTEEN

F orgive and be free. Forget that you have forgiven and be
freer - Gautama Buddha

Ọmọyẹ tried to reach out to Ikẹ, Dupẹ and Dayọ
for reconciliation after their grandmother died. All of them
went to give their grandmother a befitting burial but after
that, communication between them and their mother was
patchy. The day she heard that Tayọ had travelled out of the
country, she could not believe it. Later she found her way to
their uncle's place. Ezekiel, being who he was, welcomed
her warmly. No judgement. No hatred. She had become
very old and looked fragile.

"Mama Ikẹ, you're welcome. Long long time. How are you
doing?"

"Ezekiel, I am not doing well as you can see. It has been
litany of one bad luck or the other for me all my life. Why it

is like that for me, I don't know. Now I'm lonely. My second husband died of heart attack and things became worse for me since that time. There's been no peace of mind for me in ages."

"Sorry to hear that."

"How are your own biological children and your other children?"

"By 'other children', do you mean Ikẹ, her sisters and Tayọ?"

"Yes. You are right."

"They are all doing well. Aren't they your children anymore?"

"I know what I am talking about Ezekiel. Hum…. Hum…. They are my children. You're right about that. But if not for people like my parents, you and many other good people I never knew who raised them up, do you think they can still be alive and become anything in life? That's why I say they are all your children. I know and I accept that I have failed them as a mother. I accept my fault but…."

"But what, Mama Ikẹ?"

"Em….em….There was something that happened to me that changed my attitude to life. The result of that has affected everyone I come across ever since."

"Is it possible for you to tell me what happened."

"Yes, I will tell you today. That's why I came."

"I'm listening."

"Ezekiel. Ezekiel. Ezekiel. How many times did I call you?"

"Three times, Mama Ikẹ."

"Listen carefully. You know how my mother had only two surviving children, my brother and me. You also know how my brother mysteriously died in a palm tree climbing accident five days before his wedding."

"Yes, I do but, I don't know much about what led to his death. I just knew he died when he fell from a palm tree as you've said."

"Yes. That's the beginning of my problem with people in general. This is the full story. My father had four wives. My mother was the first wife. My younger brother and I, as I have said, were the two surviving children of our mother; all other children she gave birth to died. Two other wives gave birth to many children. The last wife was barren. I loved my younger brother from the time he was born. He loved me and he would fight others on my behalf if they tried to fight with me. I did the same for him when he was growing up. It was like that until I was married off at a young age. He was doing well as a farmer. He grew up to become a lovely young man. The time came for him to get married. A lovely young woman was arranged for him to marry. The day for the wedding was fixed. The preparation was at the top gear. Two weeks to the date, our mother had a quarrel with her husband's last wife who I told you was barren. She vowed our mother would cry over her children for having a squabble with her. Our mother did not take her threat serious but I was afraid. The elders in the village settled the quarrel for them. The effect of my brother's sudden death terribly numbed me and my mother. Though no one linked his death to my father's junior wife's threat, I held her responsible for my brother's death. Why? I will tell you. I started to look for a priest or a diviner who could tell me who killed my brother. That took me to one of the fortune tellers who was popular in our locality one day. I did not let my mother or anyone else know about my mission. My mother got over what happened it appeared, but not me.

"I went to the diviner's place one Saturday morning. The man welcomed me. He asked me to remove my headgear, my neck chain, the traditional bangles on my hand and my shoe before I entered his shrine. I did. After that, he said, 'Sit on that black mat.' I did. He cast his ọpẹlẹ[1] on the white mat on which he sat three times and said some inaudible statements. He then told me, 'My daughter, Ọrunmila, the Grand Priest of Ifá,[2] has shown me exactly who killed your brother.'

"I wanted to jump up and cry but he said, 'Stop there. No utterance must come out from your mouth. No word. No tear must come out from your eye either. No word. Do you hear me well?'

"Yes Baba," I said as I held my lips tight with my fingers.

"He continued, 'What I want to reveal to you now is between myself and you. Ọrunmila is our only witness. The day you tell anyone else, you'll die. The person you tell will die and your mother will also die. At this point, do you agree I tell you the person who killed your brother or not?'"

"Please Baba, wait. Let me go and think about it and I'll come back to give you the feedback."

"Abomination. You don't deal with Ifá like that my daughter. Once you enter this shrine, making a decision is now or never. What's your decision?" he asked firmly.

"Ezekiel, I found myself in a dilemma immediately and, fearfully, I said, 'Yes, Baba, tell me my brother's killer and I promise I will never tell anyone else about this.'

"He laughed and said, 'Hum….Hum….You're a good daughter of Ọrunmila. Your decision is accepted by Ọrunmila.'

"He cut one white bitter kola he was holding into seven pieces. He threw the kola pieces on the white mat. He made some incantations and asked me to take the kola one by one and put them inside a small black pot in front of him. I did. He poured some strange concoction in the pot and said, 'Take that black pot, speak to it what you want it to do for you today and drink the content at a go. One warning. You must not vomit a drop of anything that goes into your mouth. There must not be a drop on the floor. Now, drink.'

"I did as he ordered. Ezekiel, that was the bitterest thing I had ever drunk. Yes, it was. I almost died but I did everything not to vomit. It was hell of a drink. He then said, 'That sealed your agreement that you will never tell anyone about what you hear today.'

"Thank you, Baba," I said grudgingly.

"Now, move closer here," he commanded.

"I did. He said, 'Open this second white pot on this white mat. Look into it and tell me what you see.'

"I opened the pot with shaking hands and looked. What did I see? I saw my mother's husband's last wife making a vow inside a hut before an oracle man. She called my brother's name seven times. After the seventh time, my brother appeared in a white cloth with his hands and legs tied. His mouth was covered with a black cloth. He was looking like a statue. The evil woman then told him, 'Your mother thinks she could fight me and go free. No. You're the apple of her eyes. But I have got to kill you and cause her everlasting sorrow. Before your coming marriage, you'll go to the farm and you'll not return. Go. Ha ha ha!'

"As she said the last word, my brother disappeared. I fainted. When I came round, the Ifá Priest said, 'Yes. You have known a very powerful secret today. You've promised you'll never tell anyone. You know the repercussions. Keep to that promise or else…. Put the divination money you brought into this white cloth and go your way.'

"I staggered out of the place much more confused and afraid than I was before I went in. Since then, I fear people. I fear life. I fear that I know some truth that I must never tell anybody. I fear that I might cause the death of some people and myself. I lived with a guilty conscience. Each time I made up my mind to reveal this secret, I got angry with myself and did what I shouldn't have done. Before that unfortunate incident, I used to be happy and full of life. But after that day, I hated everything and everybody including my husband and our children because I was not happy with myself for the concealed truth. Always, it's as if I should go and strangle my brother's killer but courage failed me each time. I was dead when I'm still alive. This heavy load of guilt I carry has been too much for me."

"That's very scary Mama Ikẹ. How did you get the courage to reveal all these now?"

"Hum. That's another story. I'll tell you. I've never been a religious person all my life though I was born into a Christian family. Some few months ago, a Christian organisation came for a revival at a church in one of the villages. The revival was for three days. That was unusual though. They went to all the villages to invite people to their programme. I didn't want to go but another woman in our village who's been a Christian all her life said I must go with her one day. I agreed and went. To cut the long story short, the pastor talked so much on how people could be kept in silence and fear for life by the devil. It was as if he knew what was happening to me. After the programme, he said those who believed the devil has kept them under his grip should come out. I went out immediately. I didn't think about that decision twice. At a point, he came to where I knelt down crying. He placed his hands on my head, prayed for me and asked if there's anything I would like him to know that was making me to cry. After much assurance, I narrated my story to him but first, I told him both of us would die for telling him the secret. He said emphatically that neither of us would die. That was it. Since then, I have got the rest of mind I've never got in many years. The pastor is still alive and here I am."

"Hum….God is good."

"Yes. That personal problem, that fear that clung to me all my life, drove me out of my first husband's house. It didn't give me any rest in my second husband's house. My family tried to settle our differences in my first marriage but they failed. Our arranged marriage broke down irretrievably. I decided not to have anything to do with my own relatives again. It was hard for anyone to understand what was happening to me. I ran away to start life afresh somewhere else. I thought doing that would give me some peace, but it did not either. I carried that heavy load of guilt to my new husband's house. I'm so sorry that I have wronged everyone. But I could not just help myself."

"Hum….Mama Ikẹ, so, you've kept all this to yourself?"

"Yes. Yes. In fact, there was a time I wanted to tell your father, my mother's younger brother because he loved my mother and he was very brave but I couldn't. I didn't want to die or cause the death of another person. So, I decided long time ago to die with this secret if not for that pastor that came to my rescue and liberated me. But Ezekiel, isn't it too late for me coming out now? Do you think people will believe me? Do you think these children will forgive me?"

"Mama Ikẹ, I think, yes. People and your children will forgive you if they listen to what you've gone through."

"If they do as you've said, will God ever forgive me? I'm still afraid. I know and believe there's God somewhere."

"Please Mama Ikẹ, don't be afraid anymore. God's forgiveness is the easiest. What happened is that, for so long, you've been robbed by Satan. You've been the plaything in his hands. You're just one of his numerous victims. You need to confess sincerely to God as that pastor advised and say sorry for the wrongs you've done. He, as your Creator, knows everything about you. Not only that, He is faithful and just to forgive you your sins. That's why He's given you this opportunity to come out and share your story."

"Are you sure He will, Ezekiel?

"Yes, I'm absolutely sure."

"If so, I'm happy to hear this. I always think no one will forgive me. Em…. Hum….This life is empty. You know this truth particularly when you're coming to the end of your life's journey. I've run and run but I never got very far."

"You are right, but now, you have been set free to enjoy the rest of your life in peace," he said and promised to speak to her children as soon as possible about her case.

When Ọmọyẹ left, she was happy that at least she had been able to tell somebody very close to her what had bothered her for decades and that forgiveness was still possible. She told her stories to some other people after that. She was advised to write an individual letter of apology to each of her children which she obliged. When Tayọ got his own letter, he opened it and went straight to identify the sender. Immediately he saw 'Your mother, Ọmọyẹ,' he did not read the rest of the letter. He went to the kitchen, lit a match and burnt the letter. That night, he could not sleep well because of the anger and sorrow that the letter which he did not even read had caused. He did not tell his wife either.

"Who would have given our mother my address? Is this woman staging a comeback after all these years of abandonment of her own children? Who tells her I still see myself as her child? Well, I'd like my sisters and uncle to know what is happening. Has she forgotten that, no matter how one tries to retie a cut rope, the length will never be the same again? Human beings are funny indeed," he thought to himself.

"But you should have read the content of that letter. Maybe the message was positive or negative you don't know," his inner mind convicted him for the singed letter.

"I just don't care. Whatever the content is does not bother me," he argued to counter his inner mind.

When he got in contact with his sisters and their uncle few days later, his sisters told him they got their letters too and his uncle also informed him of what happened between him and their mother.

"Yes, your mother came to my home. She told me certain things that changed her life and made her behave the way she has been doing all this while. She wants to see all of you and apologise for every wrong she had done to you. We need to meet as there are so many things we've got to discuss about her. The sooner we do this the better," his uncle said.

"That won't be a problem Uncle. I didn't know she's gone this far looking for peace, even coming to you to make peace," Tayọ said.

Ezekiel fixed a meeting with them and their mother. At the meeting, he told them all that their mother told him and begged on her behalf for their understanding. After much persuasion, Tayọ who had once vowed never to forgive his mother was won over. Their mother cried her eyes out and begged all of them to forgive her.

"If you can do this for me, I think I can die with some peace which has eluded me all these wasted years. I'm not after getting any support from you if at all you're thinking about that. What I am after is for us to be united and for people to learn from me that, looking for a solution to one's problem in wrong places, keeping unnecessary secrets, fear, hatred and loneliness are dangerous. All of them are killers. Even if it was my father's last wife that killed my younger brother as I was made to believe, I now forgive her. If you could arrange a meeting between your father and myself, I am ready to ask for his forgiveness for the way I behaved to him during our marriage. Everything I did was beyond me. I am happy today because I have poured out my mind again and, I have some inner peace. I need this inner peace now more than ever," she said crying.

"Mama, that's okay. It is enough. We love you though it has taken this long for you to know this. Before today, we might have been very bitter with the way you have treated all of us. Listening to all you have said so far, things would have probably turned out positive if your brother had not died the way he died. If our grandmother did not have a quarrel with the other wife, if that woman had not told her she would cry over her children and if you didn't go to that Ifá Priest who you said made you to know who killed your brother. Who knows….? There are just so many ifs but….Táyò, I don't know if you have something to say," Dayọ, their eldest sister said.

"Thank you. Few things I've got to say with due respect to everyone present here today. I will start by saying I now forgive our mother. I cannot believe this is happening. I cannot believe that statement, 'I now forgive our mother', has come out from my mouth. But with God, everything is possible. What she herself has gone through is enough punishment. I thank you, our dear uncle for all that you and your family have done for us. All that you did are impossible to repay. I thank you my sisters. Despite all the challenges we have faced, we're here today to tell our story to those coming after us. Thank you, our mother, for having the guts to come out and open up. To be late is better than never." Before he said the last sentence, his sisters and their mother were sobbing. His fragile mother stood up and hugged each of them.

The children left for their various stations the following day while their mother stayed with Ezekiel for a week.

As they were eating at the dining table one afternoon, Ọmọyẹ told Ezekiel and his wife, "I have to tell the two of you this. Now that I'm free from fear and regrets, I'm ready to go back to my Maker – my God - any time He's ready to call me back home. I'm prepared."

"Mama, that will not be now. God will give you many more years to enjoy His new glory in your life," Ezekiel's wife said.

"Amen," Ezekiel said.

Two weeks after she got back to her village, the children and Ezekiel received the news that Ọmọyẹ had died peacefully in her sleep. Ezekiel cried when he heard the news because he believed she suffered alone a lot and for so many years.

His wife appealed to him to take solace in the fact that she died with peace of mind which many people did not always have when the time to die stared them in the face. She said

further, "Just two weeks ago, Mama must have had the
premonition she would die when she told the two of us
about going back to meet her Creator. I pray for her soul to
rest in peace and may the Lord comfort all of us,"

When Tayọ was informed about the sad news, he said,
"Oh….no! Oh….no! Our mother is dead? I can't believe this!
I just told my sisters few days ago that I wanted to move her
back to the city and I had phoned an agent to start looking
for a good accommodation for her. Ha! What a loss! This
life!"

Bunmi comforted him and told him he should at least be
happy that the reconciliation meeting took place before she
died.

"Death is a debt we've all got to pay at a time we never
know of. It's always painful when we lose our dear ones,"
she said.

"Hum. You've said it all. Death! *He kills one who is being called
and also kills the caller.*[3] Each time I remember this proverb, I
marvel at how much power death has on human beings
except for those who die in Christ," Tayọ said.

The children and other family members were all sorrowful
that Ọmọyẹ died just like that. Her children thought she
meant what she said during their meeting, '….I'm not after
getting any support from you if at all you're thinking about
that. What I am after is for us to be united and for people to
learn from me that, looking for a solution to one's problem

in wrong places, keeping unnecessary secrets, fear, hatred and loneliness are dangerous. All of them are killers....'

She was given a fitting burial just as they did for their grandmother which was a shock to most people who did not know that the rift between the mother and her children had been settled and that she had died with peace of mind. After the burial, the children called their father to a meeting to let him know all that their mother told them about her life and why she behaved the way she did to him. He felt bad and wished she were alive so he too could say sorry to her for the way he had treated her.

THE END

NOTES

CHAPTER 2

1. Praise poetry with many attributed epithets
2. Father
3. headmaster
4. 4 school
5. If they are young, I agree. These ones are mature and they are getting ready for marriage
6. Bad child
7. headmaster

CHAPTER 3

1. Why won't we rejoice, as we expected it to be, so it has turned out to be, why won't we rejoice?
2. Yes
3. My Lord, thank you
4. learned or educated one
5. A corrupt name given to Christians by Muslims

CHAPTER 4

1. Headmaster
2. Mr
3. A civil servant, working on behalf of government, is never found guilty

CHAPTER 5

1. My God will lift you up in Jesus' Name
2. Our God is merciful
3. What? Big lie!
4. It's a big lie
5. It's alright
6. Isn't that so?
7. You're a very intelligent boy
8. High school
9. Song: Your footsteps will reflect the sound of honour
     Your footsteps will reflect the sound of honour
     If you study conscientiously
     Your footsteps will reflect the sound of honour
     Your footsteps will reflect the sound of humiliation
     Your footsteps will reflect the sound of humiliation
     If you do not study conscientiously
     Your footsteps will reflect the sound of humiliation
     Tayọ study conscientiously
     Your footsteps will reflect the sound of honour
     Peter study conscientiously
     Your footsteps will reflect the sound of honour
     Bukọla study conscientiously
     Your footsteps will reflect the sound of honour.

CHAPTER 6

1. A spicy meat skewer

CHAPTER 7

1. Good morning
2. Wait. Or, don't you hear
3. You this boy has gone crazy
4. Ignoramus. He doesn't understand *come let me kill you* in English.

5. *one who foretells a day of death*
6. Mr
7. I'm thankful for my own

CHAPTER 8

1. He has killed me

CHAPTER 9

1. derogatory name given to students from well-educated family
2. a slap that makes you dizzy
3. Principal
4. white people
5. 'Mrs Stone, could you stop beating me with your cane or….what have I really done wrong?'

CHAPTER 10

1. Proverbs 19:21
2. A Nigerian proverb meaning, you don't talk any bad thing about a person's deformity in their presence

CHAPTER 11

1. a nickname, meaning, Father Big Stick because his big cane always rendered students' finger bones inactive for few days after he had beaten them
2. Bísí's mother
3. I'm done for
4. This is second slavery
5. We're all suffering from colonial mentality
6. Real problem has come to town!
7. I'm dead!

8. This world is spoilt
9. Please people, help me

CHAPTER 12

1. This is your face
2. A sure pretty girl
3. So, this is your face
4. Slang for assiduous students
5. But
6. Assiduous student
7. What one does not suffer for doesn't last long in one's hand
8. Slang for Papa
9. Cassava flour
10. Slang for cassava flour
11. I'm dead

CHAPTER 13

1. fraud
2. fraud
3. Assiduous student

CHAPTER 14

1. Boss
2. We love this

CHAPTER 15

1. A divination chain
2. A Yoruba religion and system of divination
3. A Nigerian proverb

Printed in Great Britain
by Amazon

85892315R00183